Canadian Landscape Painting 1670–1930

Distributed by the University of Wisconsin Press, Madison

The Artist and The Land

Canadian Landscape Painting 1670-1930

Text and Catalogue by R. H. Hubbard

Essay by Northrop Frye

Elvehjem Art Center, University of Wisconsin, Madison

Hopkins Center Art Galleries, Dartmouth College, Hanover

University Art Museum, University of Texas, Austin

Canadian Landscape Painting
Published 1973
The Elvehjem Art Center

Distributed by
The University of Wisconsin Press
Box 1379, Madison, Wisconsin 53701
The University of Wisconsin Press, Ltd.
70 Great Russell Street, London WC1B 3BY

This project is supported by a grant from the
National Endowment for the Arts in Washington, D.C.,
a federal agency. The exhibition and catalogue were
supported by a grant from the Thomas E. Brittingham Trust.

Designed by Richard Hendel

Printed in the United States of America
ISBN 0-299-97007-8; LC 72-11461

Patrons

HIS EXCELLENCY MARCEL CADIEUX

Ambassador of Canada to the United States of America

HIS EXCELLENCY ADOLPH W. SCHMIDT

Ambassador of the United States of America to Canada

Contents

Foreword

This survey of Canadian landscape painting, the first major exhibition with this special focus, has been undertaken as a tribute to the artists of Canada who have rendered the unique character of that vast country. It also represents something of a crusade to remedy the international neglect of Canadian art. The paintings, the lenders, the authors of the catalogue, and the coordinating efforts of our northern neighbor's leading art museum make this a thoroughly Canadian exhibition.

That the lenders are willing to part with so many "landmark" Canadian paintings testifies to the cooperation we have had in arranging this exhibition. We are especially grateful to them for this sharing. As a group, these seventy-four paintings form a pictorial expression of Canada's topography, and they encapsulate three hundred years of what Northrop Frye refers to as "the backbone of Canadian painting." The richest repository of Canadian painting, the National Gallery of Canada, is the principal lender.

In 1970–1971 the idea for an important exhibition of Canadian art was sparked by discussions following a trip to Montreal, where Arthur J. Frank, an Elvehjem Art Center Council member, and the Director of the Elvehjem Art Center saw the impressive Group of Seven exhibition, which had been organized by Dennis Reid of the National Gallery of Canada, and which was then on view at the Montreal Museum of Fine Arts. In subsequent discussions with Jean Sutherland Boggs, Director of the National Gallery of Canada, R. H. Hubbard, its Chief Curator, and Joanna Woods Marsden, its Coordinator of International Exhibitions, our plans for the exhibition took form. The rationale of the exhibition was developed by Dr. Hubbard, who has prepared the catalogue. Without his magical way with words, his unparalleled knowledge of Canadian painting, and his enthusiastic cooperation in this venture, the exhibition could not have been realized. The generous assistance of others on the staff of the National Gallery of Canada, particularly Mrs. Marsden who handled many of the international arrangements for the show, is acknowledged with gratitude.

The exhibition and catalogue are supported by grants from the National Endowment for the Arts, the Thomas E. Brittingham Trust, and the exhibition funds of the three sponsoring museums, for all of which we are deeply grateful.

Truman H. Brackett, Jr., Director
Hopkins Center Art Galleries, Dartmouth College

Donald B. Goodall, Director
University Art Museum, University of Texas

Millard F. Rogers, Jr., Director
Elvehjem Art Center, University of Wisconsin

Lenders

THE ART GALLERY OF HAMILTON, Hamilton, Ontario

THE ART GALLERY OF ONTARIO, Toronto

BEAVERBROOK ART GALLERY, Fredericton, New Brunswick

HART HOUSE, University of Toronto

DR. AND MRS. G. R. MC CALL, Montreal

MC CORD MUSEUM, Montreal

MRS. H. O. MC CURRY, Ottawa

MONASTÈRE DES URSULINES, Quebec

MONTREAL MUSEUM OF FINE ARTS

MUSÉE DU QUÉBEC, Quebec

THE NATIONAL GALLERY OF CANADA, Ottawa

THE PUBLIC ARCHIVES OF CANADA, Ottawa

DR. AND MRS. MAX STERN, Montreal

MRS. SCOTT SYMONS, Toronto

VANCOUVER ART GALLERY, Vancouver

Preface

At this time of heightened sensitivity on the part of Canadians to what our parsons used to call The Great Republic to the South of Us, and of the feverish search for Canadian cultural identity, it is refreshing to offer three American universities an opportunity to contemplate the solid achievements of the Canadian past rather than confronting them with the polemics of the present. This exhibition is particularly gratifying to those of us who have a long experience of both our countries. Northrop Frye, whose perceptive essay graces this catalogue, is a critic of international eminence widely honored in the United States. The present Director of the National Gallery of Canada, Miss Jean Sutherland Boggs, spent a considerable part of her career in the learned and lively circles of American art historians and actively maintains this association. I myself studied at the University of Wisconsin and cherish the fondest feelings for its Department of Art History and its new art center; and over the years I have given lectures at a number of American universities and colleges including Dartmouth.

High in this ambassadorial company we must rank the initiator of this exhibition, Millard F. Rogers, Jr., Director of the Elvehjem Art Center of the University of Wisconsin, and his colleagues at Dartmouth College and the University of Texas, who are its co-hosts: Truman H. Brackett, Jr., and Donald B. Goodall respectively. And there are many others who are like-minded in both countries. It seems to me that we who know the United States and Canada in this intimate if somewhat rarefied way are in a unique position to assess, and influence for the good, the relations between us as a whole, whether pleasant (as they usually are) or exasperating (as at times they may become).

Curious as it may seem, after all these years, this exhibition is the first serious attempt to introduce Canadian landscape painting to Americans. In our turn, to honor the bicentenary of American Independence, we hope to present in Ottawa the first major historical survey of American painting that Canadians will ever have seen. It is through an intimate knowledge of each other's "frailest leaves" and not through instinctive or erratic reactions to current events that we shall preserve our traditional friendship and advance the understanding so desperately needed among the nations of the world today.

Ottawa, September 1972   R. H. Hubbard
                                          Chief Curator
                                          The National Gallery of Canada

rower than Chile. This thrust into the interior modulated from canoe to rail, and its economic motives from furs to timber and minerals. The imaginative movement that followed it forms the bulk of what is shown here.

That is, the primary rhythm of English Canadian painting has been a forward-thrusting rhythm, a drive which has its origin in Europe, and is therefore conservative and romantic in feeling, strongly attached to the British connection but "federal" in its attitude to Canada, much possessed by the vision of the national motto, *a mari usque ad mare* [from sea to sea]. It starts with the documentary painters who, like Paul Kane, have provided such lively and varied glimpses of so many vanished aspects of the country, especially of Indian life. A second wave began with Tom Thomson, continued through the Group of Seven, and has a British Columbia counterpart in Emily Carr. (The romantic side of the movement is reflected in the name "Group of Seven" itself: there were never really more than six, in fact there were effectively only five, but seven is a sacred number, and the group had a strong theosophical bent.) One notices in these paintings how the perspective is so frequently a twisting and scanning perspective, a canoeman's eye peering around the corner to see what comes next. Thomson in particular uses the conventions of *art nouveau* to throw up in front of the canvas a fringe of foreground which is rather blurred, because the eye is meant to look past it. It is a perspective which reminds us how much Canada developed as a passage or gateway to somewhere else, being merely an obstruction in itself. Further, a new world is being discovered. There is an immense difference in feeling between north and south Canada, but as north Canada is practically uninhabited, it exists in Canadian painting only through southern eyes. In those eyes it is a "solemn land" as frightening and fantastic as the moon.

For those who settle in the country, there is no frontier on the west: the frontier is all around, and the loneliest and most frightening part of it is the part that is within the eye and mind of the settler. Except in some parts of Quebec, there is very little in Canada to compare with the grafting of a European culture in seventeenth-century New England, New York, or Virginia, which then develops with its own traditions, so that the feeling of settlement is always there as a part of one's being. In the earlier poetry of Canada, much more than in the painting, there is the sense of being completely surrounded by an indifference or a hostility that may take the form of human enemies, predatory animals, or of a desperately cold winter.

Along with the documentary painters came other painters who were reconstructing the landscape in front of them into forms of vision which had been made in Europe. These painters were mainly looking for the picturesque, the novel subject that could be presented in relatively familiar conventions. They correspond to the many examples in Canadian literature of a new life in a new world being transmitted through metrical and imaginative patterns derived from Campbell, Tom Moore, and the more solemn side of Byron. Some of them, notably Krieghoff, had a sufficiently fresh eye to be able to combine the picturesque subject with the documentary outlook. But in general the picturesque eye was an idealizing one, assimilating past experience in Europe to a future when the new world would look more like the old one.

After settlement had been accomplished, a different aspect of Canadian imagination developed, north-south in direction, and accompanied by a sense of strong dislocation, as the Canadian began to feel that he was on the fringes of a continent whose center is in the United States. This feeling turns into something shrewd, humorous, observant, the attitude of a country which is on the sidelines of history. The consciousness of being part of a vast imperial power, oppressed by the responsibility that goes with that, which the American has from birth, the Canadian does not have at all. The result is something cooler in the Canadian temperament, in which such things as the American sense of malaise and moral failure in the sixties necessarily take a more muted and toned-down form. Politically, this consciousness is longitudinal, a feeling that Canada is split into a number of northern extensions of the United States. As Quebec will not fit into this conception, it eventually becomes as isolated from it as from the more romantic and federal attitude.

Nevertheless, it is Quebec that has taken the lead in developing a pictorial consciousness which is cool, detached, urbane, and limited in objectives. There are many examples in this exhibition: the most important is the painting of Morrice, who turned the Impressionist and Fauvist techniques he had learned in Paris to very different uses from those we find in the Group of Seven. Later on, David Milne, and LeMoine FitzGerald, give us something of the same kind of feeling in English Canada. The Quebec tradition expresses itself also in some extraordinary variations of primitive painting that cannot be represented here, and it turned, more easily than English Canadian painting did, to the more abstract and post-Kandinsky structures which are also out of our present range.

For landscape, which was the backbone of Canadian painting for so long, has largely gone now, in favor of more international developments with few local features left, although in some more recent painters, notably Riopelle, I can see what I think is a powerful sense of sublimated landscape. Great imaginative developments seem to begin much as God does in the Bible, with a sense of the contrast between creation and chaos. As they subside, social conditions become more disturbed, and eventually the arts come to be preoccupied, first with reflecting the chaos about them, and then with becoming identified with it. This is happening in Canada as elsewhere, at a time when the future existence of Canada itself is still a matter of some doubt. It is a curious irony that, just as technology, with the jet plane, was beginning to make sense of the country, the political imagination, which always lumbers along in ox-carts many decades behind the world it is actually in, has become more divisive than ever. A sour little joke was circulating in Canada during the centennial year of Confederation (1967), to the effect that when Canada was formed, it was hoped to make it a combination of British political institutions, American economic buoyancy, and French culture; and that what it now appears to have, a century later, is French politics, British economic buoyancy and American culture. However, there are always more hopeful signs, and a study of the energy and precision of the Canadian pictorial imagination will lead us to one of them.

R. H. Hubbard

Landscape Painting in Canada

Sublimity is the characteristic of this western world. . . . A landscape painter might here expand his imagination

(The History of Emily Montague, *1769*)

I

It is the common lot of the lesser country living in the shadow of the greater to be constantly occupied in measuring herself up to the giant in the land. This has been Canada's experience *vis-à-vis* the United States over a good many generations. But unlike an Austria or a Belgium she has had not only a powerful neighbor-cousin but two august parents, England and France, to look up to. This "monstrous regiment" of relations was enough to instill in the gangling Child of Nations a deferential attitude towards her elders and give rise to doubts as to her own importance in the world. Like a person suffering from an inferiority complex she at times reacts with outbursts of assertiveness.

All this has affected Canada's attitude towards her own past, making the study of Canadian history a self-conscious pursuit. Even more difficult has been the history of Canadian art. As recently as thirty years ago most Anglophone Canadians were accustomed to regard early French Canadian wood carving and decorative arts as peasant crafts unworthy of being classed as Art. The same opprobrium would have been attached to early painting had anything been known about it. Americans had of course faced much the same obstacles to the study of their art somewhat earlier on; like them we have since won recognition for our early art. An artistic past, spanning three centuries and displaying an astonishing richness of production for so small a population, has been rediscovered, and Canadian studies in art are now going strong. The problem may soon be to counter the overenthusiastic inquiry into every minor artist with an insistence on some standard of quality.

Involved in this study is an investigation of the sources of Canadian art, but little has yet been attempted along these lines. From a preliminary inquiry I once made of the backgrounds of early Canadian architecture and decoration* I well know how groping can be the initial pursuit of these sources and how elusive the appropriate comparative examples. The same should be done for painting, though this would be a bigger task. I can only touch upon it lightly here.

* "The European Backgrounds of Early Canadian Art," *Art Quarterly,* XXVII, No. 3, 1964, pp. 297–323.

One difficulty in the way of the historian of Canadian art is that of his critical apparatus or lack of it. A generation ago the Canadian art historian was obliged to go abroad for professional training, and even now that Canadian universities offer such studies, he is as often as not taught by foreign scholars. This colors his view of Canadian art. Thirty years ago I returned from post-graduate studies at the University of Wisconsin under the late revered Oskar Hagen, one of the few to analyze American art for its underlying "patterns and principles." He allowed me to choose early Canadian topics for my theses. It was natural for me, in the absence of all but the most elementary literature on the subject, to apply the principles of the American development to our own situation. But like some American-trained political historians of Canada I soon had to alter my ideas in the light of the facts. As Northrop Frye points out in his essay in this catalogue, Canadians are up against quite a different heredity, environment and history from that of Americans. Contemporary Canada as a whole has, for instance, but little operative tradition going back to the seventeenth or eighteenth centuries as has the United States. Her basic character was formed in mid-Victorian times, though it was pervaded with a faint fragrance from Old France—a fact that is strikingly symbolized by the style of the Houses of Parliament in Ottawa: romantic reverie as against the classic pomp of Washington.

And so we cannot expect any consistent parallels between Canadian and American painting—any more, for that matter, than between Canadian (or American) and Latin American—in spite of occasional and striking similarities, to which I shall refer later. Our formative influences were very different. First in time came that of French art, though with the odd proviso that painting was the least of the arts in New France, lagging well behind wood carving and other crafts in quantity and importance. But later waves of French influence were to strike responsive chords in French Canada from the early nineteenth century onward; and of course the later developments of painting in France affected the entire country as international influences.

The other parental influence was from England. It came to bear on Canadian painting only after 1759, a century or so later than on American art. Thus the great portrait tradition of seventeenth and eighteenth-century England never became established here. The main impact came from English landscape painting of the later eighteenth century, which entered fortuitously through the agency of amateur topographical watercolorists who were mostly officers of the garrison. These, in a country crying out to be painted, established the primacy of landscape, which by the beginning of the twentieth century was to grow into a monopoly. Meanwhile, French Canada, with considerable difficulty, maintained a broader scope of art inherited from France.

American influences constitute a special theme in this paper* and will become evident as it proceeds. The counter-theme is the development of Canadian art along independent lines, beginning tentatively in the earlier periods and coming to a climax in the first quarter of the twentieth century. Here a general parallel is observed with American painting, in that independent trends appeared in both countries at about the same time; but they followed different courses, there being (for instance) little of "regional" or urban expression in Canada to challenge the hegemony of landscape.

II

The two colonial régimes—the French (to 1760) and the English (to 1867)—witnessed both the establishment of European art traditions in Canada and the emergence of a local flavor. As for the latter, the Jesuit Pierre Charlevoix as early as 1720 noted the "air of liberty" that was breathed by the inhabitants of New France. This independence of Europe, though on a tiny provincial scale, set its mark on Quebec sculpture of at least that date. But wood sculpture was a craft. Painting was an art impossible of cultivation in a remote colony, and its few trained exponents were birds of passage. The best of them was Claude François, an associate of Poussin, who became the Récollet, and visited his Order's Quebec house in 1670–1. Traditionally attributed to him is a very large canvas of *France Bringing the Faith to the Indians of New France (1)*. Stretching like a backdrop behind its grand allegorical figure of France is an extensive landscape of St. Lawrence scenery. Even this symbolic seventeenth-century use of landscape is virtually unique in Quebec, occurring in the backgrounds of a few other pictures and portraits; but in view of the majestic array of hills as seen from the rock of Quebec—one of the grandest city sites in the world—it is astonishing that there was no real development of landscape in New France. The only native evidence is found in several small *ex voto* paintings by folk-artists (Fig. 1).

A change came with the British conquest. Wolfe's forces in 1759 included two officers, Richard Short and Hervey Smyth, who according to the practice of the period were trained to record their surroundings with the pencil. Their views of Quebec and Halifax were later engraved and published in London. Views

---

* This discussion takes account only of American influences on and parallels to *landscape* painting in Canada. It thus omits, for example, such interesting topics as the influence of Gilbert Stuart on the portraits of Robert Field and the parallels between American and Canadian primitive portraits or between the figure paintings of Thomas Eakins and those of Robert Harris.

Figure 1. Anonymous. *Ex-voto des trois naufragés de Lévis,* 1754.
Chapelle commémorative, Sainte-Anne-de-Beaupré

drawn by French artists, dating before 1759, also exist but most of these are quite functional in character, having to do with the fortifications of Quebec and Louisbourg. It was Paul Sandby in England who advanced from lightly colored landscape drawings to what Gainsborough called "real views from Nature," thus transforming watercolor painting into an art. Several of the military artists working in Canada in the half-century following 1759—Thomas Davies *(2-5)*, James Pattison Cockburn (Fig. 2) and George Heriot *(6)*—had been his pupils or friends while he was drawing-master at Woolwich. These, during peace-time postings in Canada, painted the scenery from the Atlantic provinces to the Great Lakes. The odd one like C. R. Forrest *(8)* made such a response to the majestic sweep of the land that he must be regarded as a precursor of the Group of Seven. None in this respect could rival Davies, whose fullness of technique and personal, near-primitive vision made him the most perceptive of all. Military artists continued to be active until the final departure of the British troops in 1870–1.

One by one resident artists had set up shop in Canada. There had always been a few in Quebec, but these were joined by new arrivals there and elsewhere, from England and Europe. Some, like William Berczy of Saxony, continued the old tradition of including landscape as part of the backgrounds of portraits. Such was also the case with two neo-classic painters of early nineteenth-century Quebec, Antoine Plamondon and Théophile Hamel (Fig. 3). Canada had, however, no exponent of classical landscape, as had the United States in Washington Allston. It was only the amateurs (Fig. 4) and the gifted folk-painters like Robert Todd *(13)*, Ebenezer Birrell *(11)*, and the strangely expressive Joseph Légaré *(9,10)* who gave a new twist to landscape. They discovered aspects of the essential character of the land that so often eluded the professionals: its lonely mystery, its winter sparkle, and its autumn richness. Canadian primitives, in their French *milieu*, tended to be decorative in a somewhat more nervous and precise, or sometimes a more heraldic, way than their American counterparts. The Canadian environment indeed seemed to favor the folk-painter. The emigrant Cornish artist Robert Whale was capable not only of a relatively cultivated style *(12)* but also of something verging on the primitive (Fig. 5).

Whale was one of the few professional artists who barely succeeded in establishing themselves in pioneer Upper Canada by the middle of the nineteenth century. Another was Daniel Fowler of London (Fig. 6) who came to Upper Canada for his health in 1842 and painted in the newly cleared farmland of the Kingston district until his death half-a-century later. The Irish-born Paul Kane *(14,15)* abandoned an incipient career as a portrait painter in the Toronto district to travel down the Mississippi and eventually to Europe where he toured the galleries picking up odd bits of the styles of the Old Masters. After meeting

Figure 2. James Pattison Cockburn (1778/9–1847).
View of Quebec with Timber Depot, c.1828–30.
Watercolor. Royal Ontario Museum, Toronto

Figure 3. Théophile Hamel (1817–1877). *Portrait de l'artiste*, c.1837.
Séminaire de Québec

Figure 4. Anonymous. *View of Fredericton,* 1823.
Beaverbrook Art Gallery, Fredericton

Figure 5. Robert Whale (1805–1887). *The Canada Southern Railway at Niagara,* c.1870.
National Gallery of Canada, Ottawa

Figure 6. Daniel Fowler (1810–1894). *A Wanderer in the Woodland,* 1888.
Watercolor. National Gallery of Canada, Ottawa

George Catlin in London he returned to Toronto fired with enthusiasm to paint the Indians of the Canadian west. He realized his ambition in 1846–8 by accompanying a Hudson's Bay Company expedition to the Pacific and back. His many small sketches (which have unfortunately left Canada) are encyclopaedic in their coverage of the land and life of the Indian. They formed the basis of oils which he painted in Toronto during the fifties. William Armstrong *(20)* and William G. R. Hind *(24)* are later examples of the explorer-artists who had their counterparts in the United States—though Thomas Moran and Albert Bierstadt, who first visited the American west, had greater resources of style and technique at their command than the Canadians.

Cornelius Krieghoff *(17–19)* was a curious sort of artist. This wandering German was presumably trained at Düsseldorf, as were some Americans of the period like George Caleb Bingham and Eastman Johnson. On arrival in Canada in the 1840s he set out to portray the life of the Quebec *habitant* in picturesque and anecdotal, and often meretricious, terms and sold quantities of his pot-boilers as souvenirs to the officers of the garrison and visitors to Quebec. But his best works give unmistakable evidence that the giant scale and distinctive color of the Canadian landscape had made an impression on him. Two other Germans who settled in Montreal, Otto Jacobi *(16)* and William Raphael *(25)* in their own ways portrayed the wonders of the Canadian scene.

III

The long careers of the last two artists bridged the gap between the colonial and Confederation periods. By the sixties, in spite of the occasional defense measure, a minor war, the odd threat of annexation on the part of discontented merchants, and an American-assisted rebellion in 1837–8, the Canadian and Imperial authorities at last took the measure of their great neighbor. Fear of a victorious North after the American Civil War was what jolted the separate provinces of British North America into the uncertain union of 1867. National sentiment, which sprang up most readily in the old province of Canada (Quebec and Ontario), was reflected in the founding in Montreal in 1867 of the Society of Canadian Artists. In the two decades following Confederation two vigorous Canadian-minded governors general played a critical part in establishing art on a national basis. As they travelled through the New Dominion, Lord Dufferin and his successor Lord Lorne conceived of an art that would portray the splendors of a great land stretching from sea to sea. Both of them invited Albert Bierstadt (Fig. 7), who had first painted the American west in 1859, to Rideau

15

Hall and to meet and inspire Canadian artists. Lucius O'Brien *(21–23)* was the painter most directly affected by Bierstadt and the Hudson River School, and it was he whom Lorne and Princess Louise nominated as first president of the Royal Canadian Academy at its foundation in 1880. Canadians of this period evidently ran true to form by organizing politically against the Americans on the one hand and emulating them culturally on the other.

The artists of the Confederation period exemplify the closeness of Canadian to American art that prevailed at the time. Besides O'Brien, whose style approaches the luminism of John F. Kensett, Allan Edson *(29)* reflects the style of the Hudson River School in general and that of Asher B. Durand in particular, in the landscapes he painted in the Eastern Townships of Quebec. John A. Fraser *(27,28)* painted landscapes near Toronto, which are full of local flavor and represent the closest Canadian painting ever got to the spirit of Winslow Homer. Fraser emigrated to the United States but returned to participate in a scheme to paint western Canada, sponsored by the Canadian Pacific Railway on its completion in 1886. Others of the period included Frederic Bell-Smith (Fig. 8), another luminist, and Frederick Verner *(26),* chiefly known for his many pictures of buffalo on the prairie.

The closest approach to unanimity with American painting is provided by two Canadians who began their work towards the end of the nineteenth century. Horatio Walker's (Fig. 9) elegiac interpretations of peasant life on the Ile d'Orléans (someone has said) out-Barbizoned Barbizon. They were certainly best-sellers in New York. Contrasting with Walker's "Europeanism" was the comparative "nativism" of Homer Watson *(30,31)*. His unaffected landscapes of the southern Ontario farmland owed a debt to the earlier style of George Inness whom he evidently met in New York. It was Watson whom Oscar Wilde, on a lecture trip to Toronto in 1882, proclaimed the "Canadian Constable,"thereby directing the young painter's efforts towards an ill-advised emulation of the great English artist. Also in tune with Inness, but with the Inness of the later, "Swedenborgian" phase, was William Brymner (Fig. 10) in some of his works dating from the end of the nineteenth century.

IV

The turn of the century witnessed one of those periodic resurgences of Canadianism, which alternate with the periods of strong outside influence in Canadian history. The Canada First movement, Sir Wilfrid Laurier's resistance to Imperialism, and Sir Robert Borden's defeat of Reciprocity with the United States were

Figure 7. Albert Bierstadt (American, 1830–1902). *The Rocky Mountains,* 1863.
The Metropolitan Museum of Art, New York

Figure 8. Frederic Bell-Smith (1846–1923). *Mists and Glaciers of the Selkirks,* 1911.
National Gallery of Canada, Ottawa

Figure 9. Horatio Walker (1858–1938). *Ploughing, the First Gleam*, c.1900.
Musée du Québec, Quebec (Sketch for the canvas of 1900, *Moonrise, A Canadian Pastoral*
in the Carnegie Institute, Pittsburgh)

successive political manifestations of this many-sided and often contradictory attitude. Canadianism in the painting of the period before the First World War was its artistic reflection.

The irresistible impact of Impressionism was felt at this time equally in Canada and the United States. To Canadian artists, paradoxically, it offered an escape from dependence on other European and on American styles. Two Montreal painters, Suzor-Côté *(37)* and Maurice Cullen *(35)*, not only revealed the true light and color of the Canadian landscape through the application of the techniques of the Impressionists but to their credit rediscovered the strong contours and broad planes of our scenery, especially in winter. They were probably less dependent upon the French than was, say, Childe Hassam in the United States.

It was Post-impressionism and subsequent European movements that touched off the first significant developments in Canadian painting. Here, however, we encounter the complicating factor of expatriatism, which is not unknown to American art in the period of Whistler and Sargent. Canada's best painter thus far in her history, for the sheer quality of his work, was the Montreal-born James Wilson Morrice *(33,34)*. He spent most of his life in Paris though making periodic sketching trips to other parts of Europe, Canada, North Africa and the West Indies. His early development was affected by Harpignies and then by Whistler, and he later developed affinities to Bonnard and finally to Matisse and Marquet. In the paintings he regularly exhibited in Canada, our painters and public had their first baffling taste of the kind of painting produced for aesthetic enjoyment rather than for the sake of representation or the expression of national feeling. The near-Fauvist design of Morrice's later work was taken up by Clarence Gagnon *(52)*, Albert H. Robinson (Fig. 11) and John Lyman (Fig. 12) who were all of a younger generation. Lyman transmitted the ideal if not the actual style of Morrice to the Montreal School of the forties.

Of Morrice's contemporaries only the *émigré* Canadians, Maurice Prendergast and Ernest Lawson (Fig. 13), both members of The Eight in New York, approached the goal of Fauvism. At home, the sensitive recluse Ozias Leduc *(32)* began by painting in a quiet old-fashioned Canadian way, later adopting the Symbolist style that marks his church decorations and a few refined, poetic landscapes. Ludger Larose *(36)* also painted landscapes of Montreal and its environs in an intimate and reticent manner.

Until about 1910, if Canadian painting had any center at all, it was in Montreal. After that it shifted for a period of thirty years to Toronto, where a minor landscape school blossomed out into a movement with national connotations. A number of young artists who earned their livings in photo-engravers' studios

Figure 10. William Brymner (1855–1925). *Early Moonrise in September,* 1899.
National Gallery of Canada, Ottawa

Figure 11. Albert **H**. Robinson (1881–1956). *Moonlight, Saint-Tite-des-Caps,* 1941.
National Gallery of Canada, Ottawa

Figure 12. John Lyman (1886–1967). *Bermuda,* 1913.
National Gallery of Canada, Ottawa

were not unnaturally steeped in the *art nouveau* graphic designs they found in every issue of their favorite art magazine, *The Studio*. This initial influence, along with the Impressionist palette, some contact with the Scandinavian painters, and a few vague ideas from theosophy, combined to produce in J. E. H. MacDonald *(33,34)*, Tom Thomson *(45–51)*, Lawren Harris *(67–71)*, A. Y. Jackson* *(60–64)*, F. H. Varley *(53–55)*, Arthur Lismer *(65,66)*, Franklin Carmichael *(73)* and Frank H. Johnston *(72)* an epic manner of painting the wild northern landscape with its emphatic rhythms and its autumn colors. Thomson, a self-taught genius, painted a series of glowing sketches of Algonquin Park, a forest reserve in northern Ontario, enlarging but a few of them into tapestry-like canvases before his premature death by drowning in 1917. Jackson and Varley served as war artists in the First World War and while in London were affected by the linear expressionism of Paul Nash. In 1920 Thomson's survivors were reunited in Toronto and exhibited for the first time as the Group of Seven. For a few years they painted with remarkable unanimity as to style and subject-matter, then they went their several ways: Jackson to expressive form and Harris to dynamic form in landscape, and Varley to sensitive figure painting. From Toronto they fanned out across the whole country, discovering virgin painting grounds on the Atlantic coast and in the Laurentians, the Rockies, the Northwest Territories, and the Arctic.

Apart from them a number of painters were active in various parts of Canada and abroad. Gagnon and Robinson, already mentioned, were the most sympathetic to the Group of Seven and often exhibited with them. Lyman lived abroad until the forties. Emily Carr of Victoria *(38–40)* began as a Fauve but was converted to expressive design after contact in the late twenties with the Group of Seven (especially Harris) and probably with Mark Tobey as well. From this she advanced to the ardent swirl of her later style, which revealed a spirit in tune with the scale and fecundity of nature on the west coast.

Far removed from the austere school by temperament and training were David Milne *(56–59)* of rural Ontario, who developed a delicate personal manner in New York (Fig. 14) with some influences from Lawson or Prendergast, and L. L. Fitz-Gerald *(74)* of Winnipeg who, in spite of the precise linear nature of his style, was admitted as a member of the Group of Seven in its last year, 1932. The styles of two others, A. J. Casson (Fig. 15) and Edwin Holgate (Fig. 16), who joined the Group of Seven—which over the years fluctuated in number from six to eight—were more in accord with the accepted manner.

---

* One of Jackson's formative influences, as Jean-René Ostiguy has pointed out, was the impressionist landscape of American painters like Elmer Schofield and Edward Redfield, which he saw during a season spent in Chicago.

Figure 13. Ernest Lawson (1873–1939). *Snow-bound Boats,* c.1907.
National Gallery of Canada, Ottawa. (Exhibited at Canadian Art Club, Toronto, 1911)

Figure 14. David Milne (1882–1953). *Boston Corner* [Berkshire Hills], 1917.
National Gallery of Canada, Ottawa.

Figure 15. A. J. Casson (1898–). *Approaching Storm, Lake Superior,* 1929.
Watercolor. National Gallery of Canada, Ottawa

Figure 16. Edwin H. Holgate (1892–). *Ski Tracks,* c.1930.
Art Gallery of Hamilton

When Lawren Harris, in the mid-thirties,* crossed the boundary between expressive form in landscape and outright abstraction (Fig. 17) the fate of Canadian landscape painting was sealed. Though the followers and heirs of the Group of Seven, including several sensitive landscapists and a significant Magic Realist or two, continued their activities into recent years, the major efforts of Canadian painters have since been devoted to abstraction.† The artistic energies of French Canada, long pent up under a repressive political régime in Quebec, finally burst their bonds in the forties and found release in the surrealism of Pellan and Borduas and the abstract expressionism of Riopelle. By the mid-fifties, however, painting in all parts of the country had fallen in line with international modern art with its abrupt changes of style and Orwellian shifts of headquarters from Paris to New York and who knows where next. National landscape now seems a dead issue, though in the work of some contemporary painters it would seem to lie just below the surface. Whether it is simply a memory to be trotted out in whimsy, or whether latent in our art and waiting to be liberated, is something only the future can tell.

* Harris worked for a time in New Mexico in touch with Georgia O'Keeffe and the Transcendental Group.
†Though with little earlier preparation, as American painting had in Feininger, Dove, Stella and others.

Figure 17. Lawren Harris (1885–1970). *Abstraction,* 1940–1.
Hart House, University of Toronto

Short Bibliography

Donald W. Buchanan   *Canadian Painters from Paul Kane to the Group of Seven.* Oxford and London, Phaidon Press, 1945

Donald W. Buchanan   *The Growth of Canadian Painting.* London, Collins, 1950

J. Russell Harper   *Painting in Canada, a History.* Toronto, University of Toronto Press, 1966
French version: *La peinture au Canada des origines à nos jours.* Quebec, Presses de l'Université Laval, 1966

R. H. Hubbard   *An Anthology of Canadian Art.* Toronto, Oxford University Press, 1960

R. H. Hubbard   *The Development of Canadian Art.* Ottawa, Queen's Printer, 1963
French version: *L'évolution de l'art au Canada.* Ottawa, Imprimeur de la Reine, 1963

R. H. Hubbard and Jean-René Ostiguy   *Three Hundred Years of Canadian Art/Trois cent ans de l'art canadien* (exhibition catalogue). Ottawa, National Gallery of Canada, 1967

Peter Mellen   *The Group of Seven.* Toronto, McClelland and Stewart, 1970

Gérard Morisset   *La peinture traditionnelle au Canada français.* Ottawa, Cercle du livre de France, 1960

Jean-René Ostiguy   *Un siècle de peinture canadienne 1870–1970.* Quebec, Presses de l'Université Laval, 1971

Dennis Reid   *Le groupe des Sept/The Group of Seven* (exhibition catalogue). Ottawa, National Gallery of Canada, 1970

Catalogue by R. H. Hubbard

Abbreviations

General

AGO/AGT	The Art Gallery of Ontario, Toronto (formerly Art Gallery of Toronto)
GS	The Group of Seven. Annual exhibitions, Toronto, 1920–31
MMFA	Montreal Museum of Fine Arts (formerly Art Association of Montreal)
NGC	The National Gallery of Canada, Ottawa
OSA	Ontario Society of Artists. Annual exhibitions, Toronto, 1872–
RCA	Royal Canadian Academy of Arts. Annual exhibitions usually alternating between Montreal and Toronto, 1880–

Literature

AR	Annual Report/Annual Review
The Arts in Canada 1957	*The Arts in Canada,* Ottawa, Canadian Citizenship Branch, 1957 ff. (several editions 1958–67)
Boggs 1971	Jean Sutherland Boggs, *The National Gallery of Canada,* Toronto, Oxford University Press, 1971
Buchanan 1945	Donald W. Buchanan, *Canadian Painters from Paul Kane to the Group of Seven,* Oxford and London, Phaidon Press, 1945
Buchanan 1950	Donald W. Buchanan, *The Growth of Canadian Painting,* London, Collins, 1950
CA	*Canadian Art* (periodical); became *Artscanada* in 1967
Colgate 1943	William Colgate, *Canadian Art, its Origins and Development,* Toronto, Ryerson Press, 1943
Harper 1962	J. Russell Harper, "Three Centuries of Canadian Painting," *Canadian Art,* xix, no. 6 (no. 82), November–December, 1962, pp. 405–451
Harper 1966	J. Russell Harper, *Painting in Canada, a History,* Toronto, University of Toronto Press, 1966 (French edition, *La peinture au Canada des origines à nos jours,* Quebec, Presses de l'Université Laval, 1966)
Housser 1926	F. B. Housser, *A Canadian Art Movement: the Story of the Group of Seven,* Toronto, Macmillan, 1926
Hubbard 1957	R. H. Hubbard, "Growth in Canadian Art," in Julian Park, ed., *The Culture of Contemporary Canada,* Toronto, Ryerson Press and Ithaca, Cornell University Press, 1957, pp. 95–142.
Hubbard 1960	R. H. Hubbard, *An Anthology of Canadian Art,* Toronto, Oxford University Press, 1960.

Hubbard 1963	R. H. Hubbard, *The Development of Canadian Art,* Ottawa, Queen's Printer, 1963 (French ed., *L'évolution de l'art au Canada,* Ottawa, 1963)
Kilbourn 1966	Elizabeth Kilbourn, *Great Canadian Painting, a Century of Art,* Toronto, Canadian Centennial Publishing Co., 1966
Mellen 1970	Peter Mellen, *The Group of Seven,* Toronto and Montreal, McClelland and Stewart, 1970
Morisset 1960	Gérard Morisset, *La peinture traditionnelle au Canada français,* Ottawa, Cercle du livre de France, 1960
NGC Cat. 1960	R. H. Hubbard, *The National Gallery of Canada Catalogue of Paintings and Sculpture,* Vol. 3: *Canadian School,* Toronto, University of Toronto Press, 1960
Ostiguy 1971	Jean-René Ostiguy, *Un siècle de peinture canadienne 1870–1970,* Quebec, Les Presses de l'Université Laval, 1971
Robson 1932	Albert H. Robson, *Canadian Landscape Painters,* Toronto, Ryerson Press, 1932
VdA	*Vie des arts* (periodical)

Exhibitions

AGT 1949	*Fifty Years of Painting in Canada,* Art Gallery of Toronto, 1949
Albany 1946	*Painting in Canada, a Selective Historical Survey,* Albany Institute of History and Art, 1946
Bordeaux 1962	*L'art au Canada,* Musée de Bordeaux, 1962
Boston 1949	*Forty Years of Canadian Painting, from Tom Thomson and the Group of Seven to the Present Day,* Museum of Fine Arts, Boston, 1949
Buenos Aires 1931	Exhibition of Canadian Art, British Empire Trade Exhibition, Buenos Aires, 1931 (no catalogue)
Charlottetown 1964	*A Century of Colonial Painting/Un siècle de peinture: l'époque coloniale,* Charlottetown, Prince Edward Island, Confederation Museum and Art Gallery, 1964.
Coronation 1953	*Exhibition of Canadian Painting to Celebrate the Coronation of H. M. Queen Elizabeth* II, National Gallery of Canada, Ottawa, 1953
DPC 1945	*The Development of Painting in Canada/Le développement de la peinture au Canada 1665–1945,* Art Gallery of Toronto, 1945 (also shown at Art Association of Montreal, National Gallery of Canada and Musée de la Province de Québec)

GS 1936	*Retrospective Exhibition of Painting by Members of the Group of Seven, 1919–1933,* National Gallery of Canada, Ottawa, 1936
GS 1954	*Group of Seven,* Vancouver Art Gallery, 1954
GS 1970	*Le groupe des Sept/The Group of Seven,* National Gallery of Canada, Ottawa, 1970
Imp. Econ. Conf.	*Souvenir Catalogue* [exhibition of Canadian art], Imperial Economic Conference, Ottawa, National Gallery of Canada, 1932
London 1924	*Canadian Section of Fine Arts,* British Empire Exhibition, Wembley Park, London, 1924
London 1925	*Canadian Section of Fine Arts,* British Empire Exhibition, Wembley Park, London, 1925 (no catalogue numbers)
Mexico 1960	*Arte canadiense,* Museo Nacional de Arte Moderno, Mexico City, 1960
Pageant 1967	*A Pageant of Canada/Pages d'histoire du Canada,* National Gallery of Canada, Ottawa, 1967
Paris 1927	*Exposition de l'art canadien,* Musée du Jeu de Paume, Paris, 1927
Richmond 1949	*Exhibition of Canadian Painting, 1668–1948,* Virginia Museum of Fine Arts, Richmond, 1949 (mimeographed catalogue)
Tate 1938	*A Century of Canadian Art,* Tate Gallery, London, 1938
300 Years 1967	*Three Hundred Years of Canadian Art/Trois cent ans d'art au Canada,* National Gallery of Canada, Ottawa, 1967
US Tour 1918	*Exhibition of Paintings by Canadian Artists,* National Gallery of Canada travelling exhibition, shown at City Art Museum, St. Louis, and Art Institute of Chicago, etc., 1918–19
Vancouver 1966	*Images for a Canadian Heritage,* Vancouver Art Gallery, 1966
Washington 1950	*Canadian Painting,* National Gallery of Art, Washington, 1950
Yale 1944	*Canadian Art, 1760–1943,* Yale University Art Gallery, New Haven, 1944 (no catalogue numbers)

Paintings are oil on canvas unless noted otherwise

Attributed to Frère Luc (Claude François) 1614–1685

1 La France apportant la foi aux Indiens de la Nouvelle-France

c.1671?   86 × 86 in. (218.5 × 218.5 cm.)

Provenance:
In the Ursuline Convent, Quebec, since at least
the early 19th century. H. Magnan (see below)
reproduces a list made c.1820 by Abbé Louis-Joseph Desjardins, in which a "Découverte du
Canada" by Frère Luc is listed under "autres
tableaux" in the choir of the convent; it is thus
probable that the picture was there before the
Desjardins collection was brought to Canada
after the French Revolution.

Literature:
Joseph Sansom, *Sketches of Lower Canada, Historical and Descriptive,* New York, Kirk & Mer-
cein, 1829, pp. 90–91; Hormisdas Magnan, "Liste
des tableaux envoyés de Paris au Canada de
1817 à 1820," *Bulletin des recherches historiques,*
XXXII, no. 2, February 1926, p. 100; Gérard
Morisset, *Peintres et tableaux,* vol. 1, Quebec,
Éditions du Chevalet, 1936, pp. 19–20; *Les Ursulines de Québec 1639–1939,* Quebec, Tremblay et
Dion, 1939; Gérard Morisset, *La vie et l'œuvre
du Frère Luc,* Quebec, Médium, 1944, p. 120, no.
65; John Alford, "The Development of Painting
in Canada," *CA,* II, no. 3, March 1945, p. 99, repr,
p. 96; Marius Barbeau, *J'ai vu Québec,* Quebec,
Garneau, 1957 (no page nos.), repr.; *Hubbard
1957,* p. 116, note 24; Hubbard 1960, pl. 1;
Harper 1962, p. 408; *Hubbard 1963,* p. 47;
Harper 1966, p. 11.

Exhibitions:
DPC 1945, no. 3, repr.; London, Royal Academy,
1965, *Treasures from the Commonwealth,* no.
310; *Vancouver 1966,* no. 3; *300 Years 1967,* no. 2,
repr.; *Pageant 1967,* no. 43, repr. in color.

The English title is *France Bringing the Faith to
the Indians of New France.* It has been noted
that the figure of France bears the features of
Anne of Austria. The theory has been advanced
that the picture was commissioned c.1663–4 by
Nicolas Gargot, an adventurer on the high seas;
in which case the date of execution would be before Frère Luc's visit to Quebec in 1670–1. Cer-
tain stylistic and iconographical features (such
as the Indian huts) link this picture with *The
Martyrdom of the Jesuits* (Hôtel-Dieu, Quebec),
which is attributed to Hugues Pommier (1637–
1686). The landscape in the background is presumably of the St. Lawrence.

Monastère des Ursulines, Quebec

Thomas Davies c.1737–1812

2 On the River La Puce

1789 Watercolor
13 3/8 × 20 1/4 in. (34 × 51.4 cm.)

Inscription:
Inscribed and dated on verso, *A View of the
River La Puce near Quebec North America 1789.*

Provenance:
Earl of Derby, Knowsley, Lancs.; sold at Christie's, London, 19 October 1953, no. 137 (an album
of more than fifty watercolors); bought by
Frank T. Sabin Gallery, London; bought by National Gallery of Canada, 1954.

Literature:
NGC, *AR,* 1954–5, p. 33; *Hubbard 1963,* p. 48, pl.
76; R. H. Hubbard, "Thomas Davies, Gunner
and Artist," *Transactions of the Royal Society of
Canada,* ser. 4, IX, 1971, p. 347; R. H. Hubbard,
Thomas Davies, Ottawa, Oberon Press, 1972,
repr. in color, p. 50.

Exhibitions:
Pageant 1967, no. 174, repr.; NGC, 1972, *Thomas
Davies,* no. 53, repr.

The fall is on the little Rivière Sault-à-la-Puce,
near Château-Richer on the north shore of the
St. Lawrence below Quebec.

The National Gallery of Canada, Ottawa (6282)

Thomas Davies c. 1737–1812

3 The Falls of St. Anne

1790   Watercolor
20 3/8 × 13 9/16 in. (57.8 × 34.5 cm.)

Inscription:
Signed and dated l.r., *T. Davies Pinxit 1790;* inscribed and dated on verso, *A View of the lower
part of the falls of St. Anne near Quebec 1790.*

Provenance:
See no. 2.

Literature:
Paul Duval, *Canadian Water Colour Painting,*
Toronto, Burns & McEcheran, 1954, pl. 1; NGC,
AR, 1954–5, p. 33, repr.; "Soldier's Conquest,"
Time, LXVI, no. 12, 19 September 1955, repr. in
color p. 79; NGC, *Engagement Calendar: Water
Colours by Thomas Davies,* Ottawa, 1967, repr.
in color with a detail; R. H. Hubbard, "Thomas
Davies, Gunner and Artist," *Transactions of the
Royal Society of Canada,* ser. 4, IX, 1971, p. 347,
fig. 12; R. H. Hubbard, *Thomas Davies,* Ottawa,
Oberon Press, 1972, repr. in color, p. 53.

Exhibitions:
Pageant 1967, no. 172, repr.; NGC, 1972, *Thomas
Davies,* no. 55, repr.

The view is of the falls on the Rivière Sainte-
Anne, above Sainte-Anne-de-Beaupré.

The National Gallery of Canada, Ottawa (6283)

Thomas Davies c. 1737–1812

4 Montmorency Falls

1791   Watercolor
13 9/16 × 20 3/8 in. (34.2 × 51.7 cm.)

Inscription:
Signed and dated l.l., *T. Davies 1791;* inscribed
and dated on verso, *A View of the Montmorenci
Falls near Quebec taken in 1790.*

Provenance:
See no. 2.

Literature:
NGC, *AR,* 1954–5, p. 33; NGC, *Engagement Cal-
endar: Water Colours by Thomas Davies,* Ot-
tawa, 1967, repr. in color with a detail;
R. H. Hubbard, "Thomas Davies, Gunner and
Artist," *Transactions of the Royal Society of
Canada,* ser. 4, IX, 1971, pp. 347–8, fig. 10;
R. H. Hubbard, *Thomas Davies,* Ottawa, Oberon
Press, 1972, in color, p. 59.

Exhibitions:
Vancouver 1966, no. 15; *Pageant 1967,* no. 173;
repr.; NGC, 1972, *Thomas Davies,* no. 57, repr.

The place, seven miles below Quebec on the
north shore of the St. Lawrence, became famous
in the eighteenth century as a resort of Quebec
society, for its waterfall in summer and the ice-
cone that formed at its base in winter. Sketched
in 1790, this picture was painted after Davies' return to England late that year.

The National Gallery of Canada, Ottawa (6285)

5 Montreal

1812   Watercolor
13 1/2 × 20 5/8 in. (34.3 × 52.4 cm.)

Inscription:
Signed and dated l.r., *Thomas Davies/Delin
1812;* inscribed on verso, *Montreal.*

Provenance:
See no. 2.

Literature:
NGC, *AR,* 1954–5, p. 33; Kathleen M. Fenwick,
"Thomas Davies—Soldier and Painter of Eigh-
teenth-century Canada," *CA,* XIII, no. 3, Spring
1956, p. 276, repr. in color p. 270; *Morisset 1960,*
repr. in color opp. p. 49; *Hubbard 1960,* pl. 19;
D. G. G. Kerr and R. J. R. Robinson, *Canada, a
Visual History,* Toronto, Nelson, 1966, detail
repr. pl. 13–3; R. H. Hubbard, "Thomas Davies,
Gunner and Artist," *Transactions of the Royal
Society of Canada,* ser. 4, IX, 1971, p. 349, fig. 11;
R. H. Hubbard, *Thomas Davies,* Ottawa, Oberon
Press, 1972, repr. in color, p. 61.

Exhibitions:
Vancouver, Vancouver Art Gallery, 1959, *The
Arts of French Canada,* no. 118; *300 Years 1967,*
no. 53, repr.; *Pageant 1967,* no. 179, repr.; NGC,
1972, *Thomas Davies,* no. 63, repr.

The view is from the mountain. (Davies in 1762
painted a view from St. Helen's Island: National
Gallery of Canada.) This picture, painted the
year of the artist's death, is evidently based on
sketches made before his departure from Quebec
late in 1790.

The National Gallery of Canada, Ottawa (6286)

George Heriot 1766–1844

6   Lake St. Charles near Quebec

c.1800   Watercolor
10 11/16 × 17 1/2 in. (27.2 × 44.5 cm.)

Inscription:
Inscribed l.r., *Lake St Charles.*

Provenance:
Bought by National Gallery of Canada from
Walker, London, 1954.

Literature:
NGC, *AR*, 1954–5, p. 33, repr.; *Hubbard 1960,*
pl. 16; *Harper 1962,* repr. p. 411; *Hubbard 1963,*
p. 50, pl. 78.

Exhibitions:
Charlottetown 1964, no. 20; *Vancouver 1966,* no.
22; *300 Years 1967,* no. 42, repr.

Lac Saint-Charles is to the north of Quebec.

The National Gallery of Canada, Ottawa (6320)

Anonymous, 19th Century

7   View of Fredericton

1823   19 × 27 in. (48.3 × 68.6 cm.)

Inscription:
Signed, dated and inscribed l.r.,
M/FREDERICTON/NEW BRUNSWICK 1823.

Provenance:
William H. Coverdale Collection, Canada
Steamship Lines, Montreal (at Hotel Manoir Ri-
chelieu, Murray Bay); gift of T. R. McLagan to
Beaverbrook Art Gallery, 1959.

Literature:
John Alford, "The Development of Painting in
Canada," *CA,* II, no. 3, March 1945, p. 100, repr.
p. 96; *Buchanan 1950,* pl. 3; *Hubbard 1957,*
p. 119; Beaverbrook Art Gallery, *Catalogue,*
Frederiction, 1959, p. 32; *Hubbard 1960,* pl. 27;
Hubbard 1963, p. 52; *Arts in New Bruswick,*
Frederiction, Brunswick Press, 1967, p. 129, repr.
p. 142.

Exhibitions:
DPC 1945, no. 29, repr.; *Richmond 1949,* no. 1;
Coronation 1953, no. 1; *300 Years 1967,* no. 58,
repr.

The picture shows a portion of Fredericton from
the St. John River, probably near the Officers'
Quarters.

Beaverbrook Art Gallery, Fredericton

8 Grand Campement, French River, Lake Huron

1822 Watercolor and graphite
13 1/4 × 44 1/2 in. (33.9 × 112.7 cm.)

Inscription:
Signed and dated l.l., *C R Forrest 1822.*

Provenance:
9th Earl of Dalhousie, Governor in Chief of Canada (1819–28); William H. Coverdale Collection, Canada Steamship Lines, Montreal (at Hotel Manoir Richelieu, Murray Bay); bought by Canadian government and deposited in National Gallery of Canada, 1970.

Literature:
Percy F. Godenrath, *Catalogue of the W. H. Coverdale Collection of Canadiana,* Montreal, Canada Steamship Lines, 1930–9, no. 1799 in supplement (1939); NGC, *AR,* 1970–1, p. 96.

Exhibitions:
Montreal, Art Association of Montreal, 1940, *Historic Canadiana,* no. 1799 (as by D. W. Forrest); *DPC 1945,* no. 21 (as by D. W. Forrest).

The French River, which flows from Lake Nipissing into Georgian Bay, was on the old canoe route from Montreal to the upper lakes. The camping-place was a flat expanse near the mouth of the river.

The National Gallery of Canada, Ottawa (16649)

Joseph Légaré 1795–1855

9   Les chutes de Saint-Ferréol

c.1840   29 9/16 × 34 13/16 in. (75.1 × 88.4 cm.)

Provenance:
De Foy; Dr. Vallée, Quebec (1946); bought by
Musée de la Province de Québec, 1946.

Literature:
Mason Wade, *The French Canadians,* Toronto,
Macmillan, 1955, repr. opp. p. 177; R. H. Hub-
bard, "Primitives with Character: a Quebec
School of the Early Nineteenth Century," *Art
Quarterly,* xx, no.1, Spring 1957, p. 24, fig. 2;
Hubbard 1957, p. 117; *Morisset 1960,* p. 99; *Hub-
bard 1960,* pl. 31; *Hubbard 1963,* p. 55; *Harper
1966,* p. 82.

Exhibitions:
Quebec, Musée de la Province de Québec, 1952,
Les arts au Canada français, no. 70; Paris,
Grands Magasins du Louvre, 1958, *Arts au Canada français* (no catalogue); *Bordeaux 1962,*
no. 21; *Vancouver 1966,* no. 29; *300 Years 1967,*
no. 90, repr.

Saint-Ferréol is on the Rivière Sainte-Anne,
north-east of Quebec. See also no. 3.

Musée du Québec, Quebec (A472P)

Joseph Légaré 1795–1855

10   Les ruines après l'incendie du faubourg Saint-Roch

c.1845   37 1/2 × 49 1/2 in. (95.2 × 125.7 cm.)

Literature:
Harper 1966, p. 82, pl. 72 (color); Michel Cauchon, "L'incendie du quartier Saint-Roch (28 mai 1845) vu par Joseph Légaré," *Bulletin du Musée du Québec,* no. 10, October 1968, p. 3, note a.

Exhibitions:
MMFA, 1967, *The Painter and the New World,* no. 219, repr. in color.

The English title is *Ruins after the Fire in the Saint-Roch Quarter.* A view of the Saint-Roch quarter of Quebec, by Légaré, showing the fire itself, is in the Musée du Québec, Quebec.

Mrs. Scott Symons, Toronto

Ebenezer Birrell 1801–1888

11 Good Friends

c.1830   23 × 28 in. (58.5 × 71.7 cm.)

Provenance:
Paul Duval, Toronto; gift to Art Gallery of
Hamilton from Mrs. R. N. Steiner in memory of
her mother, Mrs. L. C. Dillon, 1965.

Literature:
Art Gallery of Hamilton Bulletin, I, no. 2, December 1965, repr. (no page numbers); *Harper
1966,* p. 133, pl. 118.

Exhibitions:
Vancouver 1966, no. 30, repr. in color; *300 Years
1967,* no. 69, repr. in color.

Probably painted on the artist's farm, Maple
Hall, at Pickering, north-east of Toronto.

The Art Gallery of Hamilton, Hamilton
(65–43–18)

Robert R. Whale 1805–1887

12 General View of Hamilton

1853   35 3/4 × 47 1/2 in. (90.8 × 120.6 cm.)

Inscription:
Signed and dated lower center (on a rock),
R. Whale/Aug 2/1853.

Provenance:
Private collection, England; Museum Book
Shop, London (1947); Gavin Henderson Gallery,
Toronto; bought by National Gallery of Canada,
1949.

Literature:
A. H. Wingfield, *The Hamilton Centennial,*
Hamilton, Centennial Committee, 1946, repr.
p. 16; NGC, *AR,* 1949–50, p. 18, repr.; R. H. Hubbard, "General View from a Lofty Eminence,"
CA, XIII, no. 2, Winter 1956, p. 233, repr.; *The
Arts in Canada 1957,* pp. 41–42; *NGC Cat. 1960,*
p. 331, repr.; *Hubbard 1960,* pl. 49; *Hubbard
1962,* p. 931; J. Russell Harper, "Ontario Painters
1846–1867," *NGC Bulletin,* I, no. 1, May 1963,
p. 24, repr. p. 21; *Hubbard 1963,* p. 61, pl. 100;
Harper 1966, p. 142, pl. 130.

Exhibitions:
London, International Exhibition, 1862 (silver
medal); *Charlottetown 1964,* no. 44, repr.; *300
Years 1967,* no. 114, repr.; Brantford, Art Gallery
of Brantford, 1969, *Robert Whale,* no. 4.

The view is from the Escarpment looking north-
west towards Burlington Bay, Lake Ontario. Another view of Hamilton (69 × 39 in.) was exhibited at Brantford (see above) in 1969.

The National Gallery of Canada, Ottawa (4950)

R. C. Todd 1809–c.1865

13   The Ice Cone, Montmorency Falls

c.1845   13 1/2 × 18 in. (34.3 × 45.7 cm.)

Inscription:
Signed l.r., *R. C. Todd.*

Provenance:
Bought by National Gallery of Canada from
Laing Galleries, Toronto, 1957.

Literature:
NGC, *AR,* 1957–8, p. 56, repr.; *CA,* xv, no. 1 (no.
59), January 1958, repr. in color p. 55; *NGC Cat.
1960,* p. 313, repr.; NGC, *Engagement Calendar,*
Ottawa, 1962, pl. 27 (color); *Hubbard 1962,*
p. 932, repr.; *Hubbard 1963,* p. 55; *American
Heritage,* xvii, no. 1, December 1965, repr. in
color on cover; *Revue des voyages,* special no.:
"Canada," 1965, repr. in color p. 63; *CA,* xxvi,
no. 1 (nos. 128–9), February 1969, repr. On title-
page and details on cover; *Boggs 1971,* pl. 107;
Michel Cauchon, *Roy-Audy,* Quebec, Ministère
des Affaires culturelles, 1971, pl. iii–2.

Exhibitions:
Toronto, Laing Galleries, 1959, *One Hundred
Years of Canadian Painting,* no. 2, repr.; *300
Years 1967,* no. 70, repr.; London, Ont., Public Li-
brary and Art Museum, 1967, *The Artist in
Early Canada* (no catalogue nos.), repr.

For Montmorency Falls see no. 4.

The National Gallery of Canada, Ottawa (6763)

Paul Kane 1810–1871

14   Fort Garry and St. Boniface

1851–6   18 × 29 in. (45.7 × 73.7 cm.)

Provenance:
This is one of a group of twelve pictures commissioned by the Legislature of Canada in 1851 and delivered in 1856. Of these, five, including this picture, were transferred to the National Gallery of Canada from Parliament, Ottawa, in 1888; one was lost at an early date; and the remaining six (including no. 15) were transferred to the National Gallery in 1955.

Literature:
Paul Kane, *Wanderings of an Artist,* London, Longmans, 1859, repr. in woodcut pl. 5, opp. p. 74; Canada, House of Commons, *Sessional Papers,* 1889, p. 189; Paul Kane, *Wanderings of an Artist,* Toronto, Radisson Society, 1925, p. 1 (as "Part of Red River Settlement"), repr. in woodcut p. 50; *NGC Cat. 1960,* p. 153, repr.; *Hubbard 1963,* p. 61, pl. 99; J. Russell Harper, *Paul Kane's Frontier,* Toronto, University of Toronto Press, 1971, p. 281, no. IV–38 (as "Red River Settlement," a replica of the version in the Royal Ontario Museum, Toronto).

Exhibitions:
Ottawa, Public Archives of Canada, 1911–33 (on loan); AGT, 1933–4, *Toronto Centennial Exhibition,* no. 112; *Tate 1938,* no. 125; *Charlottetown 1964,* no. 54, repr.; *300 Years 1967,* no. 101, repr.; Fort Worth, Amon Carter Museum of Western Art, etc., 1971–2, *Paul Kane,* no. 41.

The canvases in the Royal Ontario Museum, Toronto, and the National Gallery of Canada, were based on an oil-on-paper sketch made in June 1846 and now in the Stark collection (Harper IV–36). The National Gallery of Canada version was formerly titled erroneously "Fort Garry and Bonaventure." Fort Garry, on the site of present-day Winnipeg, was rebuilt in 1838, replacing earlier forts; the gate (beside the Fort Garry Hotel) is the only part still standing. On the St. Boniface side of the Red River (at left) the Grey Nuns' Convent of 1846 still stands; but the Cathedral of 1833–7 was destroyed by fire in 1860; it is known from Whittier's couplet in *The Red River Voyageur:*

The bells of the Roman Mission
That call from their turrets twain.

The National Gallery of Canada, Ottawa (102)

Paul Kane 1810–1871

15 Buffalo at Sunset

1851–6   16 1/2 × 27 1/4 in. (41.9 × 69.2 cm.)

Provenance:
See no. 14.

Literature:
Paul Kane, *Wanderings of an Artist,* London,
Longmans, 1859, repr. in woodcut pl. 6; Paul
Kane, *Wanderings of an Artist,* Toronto, Radis-
son Society, 1925, p. xlix, repr. in woodcut pl. 6;
NGC Cat. 1960, p. 154, repr.; *Hubbard 1960,* pl.
43; J. Russell Harper, *Paul Kane's Frontier,*
Toronto, University of Toronto Press, 1971,
p. 291, no. IV–243 (as a replica of the version in
the Royal Ontario Museum, Toronto).

Exhibitions:
Charlottetown 1964, no. 63, repr.; Waterloo,
Ont., University of Waterloo, 1968, *Paul Kane*
(no catalogue nos.).

The versions of this subject in the Royal Ontario Museum, the National Gallery of Canada
and elsewhere (see Harper, *Paul Kane's Frontier,
loc. cit.*) were all based on sketches made sixteen
miles west of Fort Edmonton on October 6, 1846.

The National Gallery of Canada, Ottawa (6919)

Otto R. Jacobi 1812–1901

16 Canadian Autumn

1870   36 × 54 1/8 in. (91.4 × 137.5 cm.)

Inscription:
Signed and dated l.r., *O. R. Jacobi 1870.*

Provenance:
Bought by Art Association of Montreal from the
William Gilman Cheney Fund, 1940.

Literature:
John Steegman, *Catalogue of Paintings,* Montreal, Montreal Museum of Fine Arts, 1960,
p. 21.

This picture was probably painted from sketches
made in the autumn of 1869, when Jacobi accompanied Prince Arthur's party on a trip up
the Ottawa River.

Montreal Museum of Fine Arts, Montreal (717)

Cornelius Krieghoff 1815–1872

17   Winter Landscape

1849   38 1/2 × 51 in. (97.8 × 129.5 cm.)

Inscription:
Signed and dated l.r., *C Krieghoff/1849.*

Provenance:
John Young, Quebec; the Hon. W. C. Edwards,
Ottawa; Miss Edith Wilson, Ottawa; gift of Miss
Edith Wilson to National Gallery of Canada,
1923, in memory of the Hon. W. C. and Mrs. Ed-
wards.

Literature:
NGC, *AR,* 1922–3, p. 13, repr.; Marius Barbeau,
Cornelius Krieghoff, Toronto, Macmillan, 1934,
p. 104; Marius Barbeau, "Krieghoff Discovers
Canada," *Canadian Geographical Journal,* VIII,
no. 3, March 1934, repr. in color opp. p. 112;
A. H. Robson, *Cornelius Krieghoff,* Toronto,
Ryerson Press, 1937, pl. iii (color); D. W. Bu-
chanan, "The Story of Canadian Art," *Cana-
dian Geographical Journal,* XVII, no. 6,
December 1938, repr. in color p. 283; Regina
Shoolman and Charles E. Slatkin, *The Enjoyment of Art in America,* Philadelphia and New
York, Lippincott, 1942, p. 691, pl. 708; John Alford, "The Development of Painting in Canada,"
CA, II, no. 3, March 1945, p. 95, repr. in color p.
101; Marius Barbeau, *Cornelius Krieghoff,*
Toronto, Ryerson Press, 1948, repr. in color opp.
p. 10; *Buchanan 1950,* pl. 2; *Encyclopaedia Canadiana,* 1958, vol. 8, pl. 96–b; *NGC Cat. 1960,
p. 163, repr.;* Marius Barbeau, *Cornelius Krieghoff,* Toronto, McClelland and Stewart, 1962, pl.
14; *Hubbard 1963,* p. 60.

Exhibitions:
AGT, 1926, *Inaugural Exhibition,* no. 192; NGC,
1934, *Cornelius Krieghoff,* no. 91; *Tate 1938,* no.
130; *DPC 1945,* no. 58, repr.; *Albany 1946,* no. 25,
repr.; Detroit Institute of Arts, 1946, *The Arts of
French Canada,* no. 228; *Washington 1950,* no.
45, repr.; Detroit Institute of Arts, 1951, *The
French in North America,* no. 88; *Coronation
1953,* no. 32; *300 Years 1967,* no. 106, repr.

Marius Barbeau (1934) identifies the figures in
the sleigh as the artist's wife Louise, his daughter Emily and Louise's father, Gauthier, at Lon-
geuil near Montreal. Radiographs of the canvas
reveal that the landscape was painted over the
portrait of an officer with a horse.

The National Gallery of Canada, Ottawa (2038)

18 The Chaudière

1858? 20 1/4 × 29 1/2 in. (51.5 × 75 cm.)

Inscription:
Signed l.r. (on a rock ledge), *C. Krieghoff.*

Provenance:
The Hon. W. C. Edwards, Ottawa; Miss Edith
Wilson, Ottawa; gift of Miss Edith Wilson to
National Gallery of Canada, 1923, in memory of
the Hon. W. C. and Mrs. Edwards.

Literature:
AR, 1922–3, p. 13; Marius Barbeau, *Cornelius
Krieghoff,* Toronto, Macmillan, 1934, p. 118;
Marius Barbeau, "Krieghoff découvre le Can-
ada," *Mémoires de la Société Royale du Canada,*
3ᵉ sér., XXVIII, 1934, p. 117; Marius Barbeau,
"Krieghoff Discovers Canada," *Canadian
Geographical Journal,* VIII, no. 3, March 1934,
repr. p. 108; *NGC Cat. 1960,* p. 162, repr.; Marius
Barbeau, *Cornelius Krieghoff,* Toronto, Ryerson
Press, 1948, p. 16; Marius Barbeau, *Cornelius
Krieghoff,* Toronto, McClelland and Stewart,
1962, p. 11, pl. 25.

Exhibitions:
NGC, 1934, *Cornelius Krieghoff,* no. 92; AGT,
1934, *Cornelius Krieghoff,* no. 273; Fredericton,
Beaverbrook Art Gallery, 1961, *Cornelius
Krieghoff,* no. 24; *Charlottetown 1964,* no. 28;
Quebec, Musée du Québec, 1971, *Cornélius
Krieghoff,* no. 54, repr. (as "La rivière Chau-
dière").

The subject is usually identified with the Chaudière Falls in the Ottawa River between Ottawa
and Hull; but perhaps, as indicated in the Quebec exhibition 1971 (above), they are the falls on
the Chaudière River near Quebec. Marius Barbeau (1934) states that the date *58* appears with
the signature and that Krieghoff travelled to
Ottawa in 1858; also that the figure among the
rocks is a self-portrait.

The National Gallery of Canada, Ottawa (2037)

Cornelius Krieghoff 1815–1872

19 The Owl's Head, Memphremagog

1859   17 1/4 × 24 in. (43.8 × 61.1 cm.)

Inscription:
Signed and dated l.r., *C. Krieghoff./Quebec 1859;*
inscribed on stretcher, *The Owl's Head Mountain (2800 ft.)/Skinners Cove on/Lake Memphremagog, Canada East./in autumnal foliage.*

Provenance:
Dr. George Hall, Montreal; Johnson Art Galleries, Montreal (1934); Vincent Massey, Port Hope, Ontario; bequest of the Right Hon. Vincent Massey to National Gallery of Canada, 1968.

Literature:
Marius Barbeau, *Cornelius Krieghoff,* Toronto, Macmillan, 1934, p. 121; Marius Barbeau, "Krieghoff Discovers Canada," *Canadian Geographical Journal,* VIII, no. 3, March 1934, pp. 112–13, repr. p. 100; Marius Barbeau, *Cornelius Krieghoff,* Toronto, McClelland and Stewart, 1962, pl. 30 (color); Hugo McPherson, "The Resonance of Batterwood House," *CA,* XXI, no. 2 (no. 90), March–April 1964, p. 98, repr.; NGC, *AR,* 1968–9, p. 65, repr.; *Boggs 1971,* pl. 109 (color).

Exhibitions:
AGT, 1934, *The Collection of Hon. Vincent and Mrs. Massey,* no. 130; NGC, 1934, *Cornelius Krieghoff,* no. 55; AGT, 1934, *Cornelius Krieghoff,* no. 226; *300 Years 1967,* no. 117, repr.; NGC, 1968, *Vincent Massey Bequest: the Canadian Paintings,* no. 23, repr.

Lake Memphremagog is in the Eastern Townships of Quebec, touching on Vermont. Owl Head Mountain is 30 miles south-east of Granby, Quebec. See also no. 29.

The National Gallery of Canada, Ottawa (15490)

William Armstrong 1822–1914

20   Silver Islet, Seen from the Mainland

1869   Pastel
14 1/4 × 24 1/2 in. (36.2 × 61.6 cm.)

Inscription:
Signed and dated l.l., *Armstrong/69.*

Provenance:
Bought by Public Archives of Canada.

Literature:
"Silver Island, Lake Superior," *Canadian Illustrated News,* December 3, 1870, p. 361, repr. by photolithography.

Silver Islet is near Thunder Cape, at the entrance to Thunder Bay, Lake Superior. Silver-mining there yielded considerable quantities of ore c.1870.

The Public Archives of Canada, Ottawa
(C10508)

L. R. O'Brien 1832–1899

21 Sunrise on the Saguenay

1880   34 1/2 × 49 1/2 in. (87.6 × 125.7 cm.)

Inscription:
Signed and dated l.r., *L. R. O'Brien 1880.*

Provenance:
Deposited in National Gallery of Canada as the
artist's Royal Canadian Academy diploma, 1882.

Literature:
Canada, House of Commons, *Sessional Papers,*
1884, p. 369; *NGC Cat. 1960,* p. 405, repr.; *Harper
1962,* p. 422, repr. p. 421; NGC, *Engagement Calendar,* Ottawa, 1962, pl. 23 (color); *Hubbard
1962,* p. 934; *Harper 1966,* pp. 177, 197, pl. 158
(color); *Kilbourn 1966,* p. 33, repr. in color; *Mellen 1970,* p. 3, repr. p. 2; R. H. Hubbard, "Ninety-
year Perspective," *VdA,* no. 58, Spring 1970,
p. 23, repr.; *Praeger Encyclopaedia of Art,* New
York, Praeger, 1971, repr. vol. 1, p. 34; *Boggs
1971,* pp. 3, 23, pl. xxii (color); *Ostiguy 1971,*
p. 16, pl. 7.

Exhibitions:
RCA, 1880, no. 115; Montreal, Art Association of
Montreal, *Special Exhibition,* 1880, no. 18; RCA,
1881, no. 268; NGC, 1941, *60th Anniversary Exhibition* (no cat.); NGC, 1952, *Royal Canadian
Academy Diploma Works* (no cat.); RCA, 1954,
Retrospective Exhibition, no. 4; *Bordeaux 1962,*
no. 9; *Vancouver 1966,* no. 42, repr.; *300 Years
1967,* no. 141, repr.

The view is of Cap Trinité on the River Sa-
guenay. The picture appears in a woodcut illus-
tration of the opening of the Royal Canadian
Academy in Ottawa, in *Canadian Illustrated
News,* March 20, 1880. A drawing for the subject
is in the Art Gallery of Ontario, Toronto.

The National Gallery of Canada, Ottawa (113)

L. R. O'Brien 1832–1899

22   Kakabeka Falls, Kaministikwia River

1882   32 1/2 × 48 in. (82 × 121.9 cm.)

Inscription:
Signed and dated l.r., *L. R. O'Brien 1882.*

Provenance:
Jenkins, Montreal; bought by National Gallery
of Canada from Percy F. Godenrath, Ottawa,
1935.

Literature:
George M. Grant, *Picturesque Canada,* Toronto,
Belden Bros., 1882, vol. 1, engr. p. 270; NGC, *AR,*
1935–6, p. 16, repr.; *Colgate 1943,* repr. p. 33; *The
Arts in Canada 1957,* p. 53, repr.; *NGC Cat.
1960,* p. 238, repr.; *Hubbard 1960,* pl. 60; *Hubbard 1963,* p. 67, pl. 107; Peter Brieger *et al., Art
and Man,* Toronto, Rinehart and Winston, 1964,
vol. 3, fig. 176; *Kilbourn 1966,* p. 33.

Exhibitions:
OSA, 1882, no. 29; RCA, 1882, no. 49; *Tate 1938,*
no. 171; *Richmond 1949,* no. 57; *300 Years 1967,*
no. 146, repr.

Kakabeka Falls are to the west of Thunder Bay,
Ontario.

The National Gallery of Canada, Ottawa (4255)

L. R. O'Brien 1832–1899

23   A British Columbian Forest

1888   Watercolor
21 1/4 × 30 in. (54 × 76.2 cm.)

Inscription:
Signed and dated l.l., *L. R. O'Brien/1888.*

Provenance:
Bought by National Gallery of Canada, 1888.

Literature:
Canada, House of Commons, *Sessional Papers,*
1889, p. 203; *NGC Cat. 1960,* p. 236, repr.; *Hubbard 1960,* pl. 58; *Hubbard 1962,* p. 934; *Hubbard
1963,* p. 67, pl. 106; *Ostiguy 1971,* pl. 6.

Exhibitions:
RCA, 1889, no. 129; OSA, *Retrospective Exhibi-
tion,* 1947, no. 147; *Mexico 1960,* no. 91, repr.; *300
Years 1967,* no. 156, repr.; NGC travelling exhibi-
tion, 1970–1, *Canadian Water-colours of the 19th
Century,* no. 23.

The National Gallery of Canada, Ottawa (159)

William G. R. Hind 1833–1888

24   Foot of the Rocky Mountains

1862   Watercolor
8 3/4 × 12 1/4 in. (22.3 × 31.1 cm.)

Provenance:
David Ross McCord, Montreal.

Literature:
Harper 1962, repr. in color p. 416; *Harper 1966,*
pl. 145.

Exhibitions:
NGC and Montreal, McCord Museum, 1962–3,
Everyman's Canada, no. 116, repr. in color.

The picture was painted near Yellowhead Pass
on the present boundary between Alberta and
British Columbia. Here the "Overlanders of '62,"
whose expedition Hind accompanied, entered the
Rocky Mountains.

McCord Museum, Montreal (M466)

William Raphael 1833–1914

25 Indian Encampment on the Lower St. Lawrence

1879   23 1/4 × 41 1/4 in. (59 × 104.8 cm.)

Inscription:
Signed and dated l.l., *W. Raphael/1879/Mon-
treal.*

Provenance:
Deposited in National Gallery of Canada as the
artist's Royal Canadian Academy diploma, 1882.

Literature:
Canada, House of Commons, *Sessional Papers,*
1884, p. 369; *NGC Cat. 1960,* p. 409, repr.

Exhibitions:
Montreal, Art Association of Montreal, 1880,
Special Exhibition, no. 9; RCA, 1880, no. 68;
RCA, 1881, no. 322; RCA, 1954, *Retrospective
Exhibition,* no. 5; London, Ont., Public Library
and Art Museum, 1967, *The Artist in Early Can-
ada* (no cat.).

The National Gallery of Canada, Ottawa (59)

F. A. Verner 1836–1928

26 Indian Camp

1876   32 1/2 × 60 in. (82 × 152.4 cm.)

Inscription:
Signed and dated l.r., *F. A. Verner/1876.*

Provenance:
Gift to Art Gallery of Hamilton from the
Women's Committee, 1964.

Literature:
Art Gallery of Hamilton, *Art Gallery News,* XII,
no. 1, July 1964, repr. (no page numbers); Art
Gallery of Hamilton, *Handbook,* Hamilton, 1964,
repr. p. 8; *Kilbourn 1966,* p. 59, repr. in color.

Exhibitions:
?OSA, 1876 or 1877 (one of a number of "Indian
Camps" exhibited); *300 Years 1967,* no. 131, repr.

Art Gallery of Hamilton, Hamilton (64–112–J)

J. A. Fraser 1838–1898

27   A Shot in the Dawn

1873   16 × 30 in. (40.7 × 76.2 cm.)

Inscription:
Signed and dated l.l., *J. A. FRASER 1873.*

Provenance:
Brought by National Gallery of Canada from
Dominion Gallery, Montreal, 1958.

Literature:
NGC, *AR,* 1958–9, p. 59, repr.; *NGC Cat. 1960,*
p. 93, repr.; *CA,* xvii, no. 1 (no. 67), January
1960, repr. p. 37; *Hubbard 1960,* pl. 57; NGC, *Engagement Calendar,* Ottawa, 1962, pl. 19 (color);
Hubbard 1962, p. 934; *Hubbard 1963,* p. 67, pl.
102; *Kilbourn 1966,* p. 37, repr. in color pp. 36–7;
Ostiguy 1971, pl. 1.

Exhibitions:
OSA, 1876, no. 38; *300 Years 1967,* no. 129, repr.
in color.

The picture has formerly been called "Lake Scugog" and "A Shot at Dawn." Lake Scugog is to
the north-east of Toronto.

The National Gallery of Canada, Ottawa (6938)

J. A. Fraser 1838–1898

28   The Rogers Pass

1886   22 × 30 in. (55.9 × 76.2 cm.)

Inscription:
Signed l.l., *JA* (in monogram) *FRASER*.

Provenance:
Sir Edwin Watkin, Bt. (President of the Canadian Pacific Railway 1882–8); bought by National Gallery of Canada from Captain Percy Godenrath, Ottawa, 1934.

Literature:
NGC, *AR,* 1934–5, p. 18, repr.; D.W. Buchanan, "The Story of Canadian Art," *Canadian Geographical Journal,* XVII, no. 6, December 1938, repr. p. 274; *NGC Cat. 1960,* p. 92, repr.; *Hubbard 1960,* pl. 61; René Huyghe, ed., *Larousse Encyclopaedia of Modern Art,* London, Hamlyn, 1961, repr. p. 236; *Hubbard 1962,* p. 934; *Hubbard 1963,* p. 67, pl. 105; *Kilbourn 1966,* repr. in color p. 10; Elizabeth Collard, "The Father of British Columbia," *Country Life,* CXLIX, no. 3856, May 6, 1971, repr. p. 1076.

Exhibitions:
Tate 1938, no. 65; *DPC 1945,* no. 66; *Richmond 1949,* no. 24; St. John's, Memorial University, and Bermuda Society of Arts, 1961, *150 Years of Canadian Art; Vancouver 1966,* no. 46, repr.; *300 Years 1967,* no. 154, repr.

Painted in 1886 when the Canadian Pacific Railway was completed. The Rogers Pass at the summit of the Selkirk Range of the Rocky Mountains was one of the most formidable barriers in the path of the railway, and surmounting it was one of the engineering feats of the age.

The National Gallery of Canada, Ottawa (4227)

29 Mount Orford and the Owl's Head from Lake Memphremagog

1870 36 × 60 in. (91 × 152.4 cm.)

Inscription:
Signed and dated l.r., *ALLAN EDSON / 1870.*

Provenance:
Andrew Wilson, Montreal; bought by National
Gallery of Canada from W. Scott & Sons, Mon-
treal, 1917.

Literature:
Art Journal, January 1, 1871, p. 8 (as "Summer
View of Mount Orford and Pond, Eastern Town-
ships"); Canada, House of Commons, *Sessional
Papers,* 1918, p. 182; *CA,* IV, no. 3, May 1947,
repr. p. 98; *The Arts in Canada 1957,* p. 53; *NGC
Cat. 1960,* p. 80, repr.; *Hubbard 1960,* pl. 56;
Hubbard 1963, p. 64, pl. 103.

Exhibitions:
Montreal, Art Association of Montreal, 1872,
Seventh Exhibition, no. 47;? Montreal, Art Association of Montreal, 1880, *Special Exhibition,* no.
64; RCA 1916, no. 72; *DPC 1945,* no. 52; *Mexico
1960,* no. 94; NGC travelling exhibition, 1962–3,
Painting in Canada (no cat.); *300 Years 1967,*
no. 125, repr.

Orford Mountain is a little to the north of Lake
Memphremagog (see no. 19).

The National Gallery of Canada, Ottawa (1398)

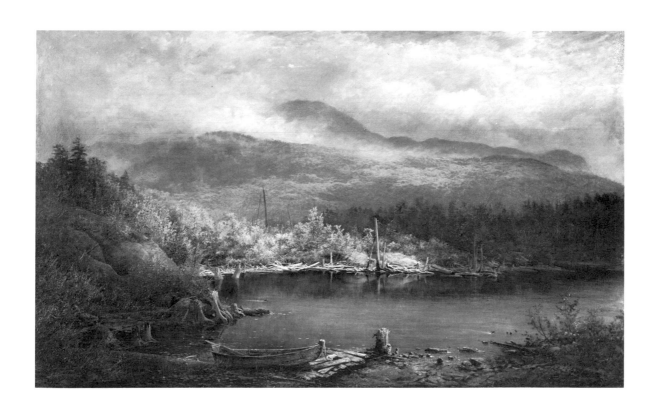

Homer Watson 1855–1936

30   On the Grand River at Doon

c.1881   23 7/8 × 36 in. (60.5 × 91 cm.)

Inscription:
Signed l.l., *Homer Watson.*

Provenance:
Private collection, England; bought by National
Gallery of Canada from Appleby Bros., London,
1952.

Literature:
R. H. Hubbard, "Two Old Masters of Canadian
Painting, Horatio Walker and Homer Watson,"
Educational Record of the Province of Quebec,
LXXI, 1955, p. 9, repr. p. 8; *Hubbard 1957,*
p. 121, pl. vii; *The Arts in Canada 1957,* p. 61,
repr.; *NGC Cat. 1960,* p. 329, repr.; *Hubbard
1960,* pl. 66; *Hubbard 1962,* p. 934; *Hubbard
1963,* p. 77.

Exhibitions:
OSA, 1881, no. 150 (as "Grand River at Doon");
RCA, 1881, no. 251; *Coronation 1953,* no. 69,
repr.; NGC, 1963, *Homer Watson,* no. 8, repr.;
300 Years 1967, no. 144, repr.

The picture was painted near the village of
Doon, the artist's birthplace and home, on the
Grand River near Kitchener, Ontario.

The National Gallery of Canada, Ottawa (5900)

31   The Laurentides

1882   25 1/2 × 41 1/2 in. (64.8 × 105.4 cm.)

Inscription:
Signed and dated l.l., *Homer Watson 1882.*

Provenance:
Deposited in National Gallery of Canada as the artist's Royal Canadian Academy diploma, 1882.

Literature:
Canada, House of Commons, *Sessional Papers,* 1884, p. 369 (as "Down in the Laurentides"); M. W. Miller, *Homer Watson,* Toronto, Ryerson Press, 1938, p. 135; R. H. Hubbard, "Two Old Masters of Canadian Painting, Horatio Walker and Homer Watson," *Educational Record of the Province of Quebec,* LXXI, 1955, p. 9; *Hubbard 1963,* p. 77; *Boggs 1971,* p. 3, pl. 112.

Exhibitions:
RCA, 1882, no. 56; RCA, 1883, no. 83; NGC, 1963, *Homer Watson,* no. 12, repr. in color; *300 Years 1967,* no. 145, repr.

The picture was painted on the lower St. Lawrence where the Laurentian mountains (Laurentides) touch the north shore.

The National Gallery of Canada, Ottawa (122)

32   Neige dorée

1916   54 × 30 in. (137.2 × 76.2 cm.)

Inscription:
Signed and dated l.r., *O. LEDUC 1916.*

Provenance:
Bought by National Gallery of Canada from
Royal Canadian Academy exhibition, 1916.

Literature:
H. Mortimer-Lamb, "The Thirty-eighth Exhibi-
tion of the Royal Canadian Academy of Arts,"
International Studio, LXX, no. 287, February
1917, p. 32, repr. p. 31; Jean Chauvin, *Ateliers,*
Montreal, Louis Carrier, 1927, p. 125; Pierre de
Ligny Boudreau, "Ozias Leduc of Saint-Hilaire,"
CA, x, no. 4, Summer 1953, repr. p. 157; *Kilbourn
1966,* p. 118, repr. in color.

Exhibitions:
Montreal, Bibliothèque Saint-Sulpice, 1916,
Ozias Leduc, no. 8; RCA, 1916, no. 134; AGT,
1926, *French Canada,* no. 214; *Paris 1927,* no.
106; *Buenos Aires 1931;* NGC, 1955, *Ozias
Leduc,* no. 26, repr. (wrongly dated 1918); Victo-
ria, Art Gallery of Victoria, 1958, *Canadian
Painting,* no. 11; *Mexico 1960,* no. 100.

The English title is *Golden Snow.*

The National Gallery of Canada, Ottawa (1368)

James Wilson Morrice 1865–1924

33 Ice Bridge over the St. Lawrence

c.1908   23 5/8 × 34 3/4 in. (60 × 88.3 cm.)

Inscription:
Signed l.r., *J. W. Morrice.*

Provenance:
Gift of the artist's executors to Art Association of Montreal, 1925.

Literature:
Donald W. Buchanan, *James Wilson Morrice,* Toronto, Ryerson Press, 1936, p. 157; *Buchanan 1950,* p. 25, repr. in color as frontispiece; John Steegman, *Catalogue of Paintings,* Montreal Museum of Fine Arts, 1960, p. 28; *Hubbard 1960,* pl. 75 (color) (dated c.1907); Kathleen Daly Pepper, *James Wilson Morrice,* Toronto, Clarke-Irwin, 1966, p. 86.

Exhibitions:
Paris, Société Nationale des Beaux-Arts, 1908; Montreal, Art Association of Montreal, 1925, *James W. Morrice,* no. 3; AGT, 1926, *Inaugural Exhibition,* no. 271; *Paris 1927,* no. 142; *Imp. Econ. Conf. 1932,* no. 10; AGT, 1935, *Loan Exhibition,* no. 135; NGC, 1937, *James Wilson Morrice,* no. 9; San Francisco, Golden Gate Exposition, 1939, *Contemporary Art,* Canada, no. 19; Hamilton, Art Gallery of Hamilton, 1953, *Inaugural Exhibition,* no. 41, repr.; Venice, XXIX Biennale, 1958, Canada, no. 10; *Mexico 1960,* no. 101, repr.; London, Ont., Public Library and Art Museum, 1965, *Canadian Impressionists,* 1965, no. 32.

A study for the composition (panel, 7 × 9 in.) is in the Montreal Museum of Fine Arts.

Montreal Museum of Fine Arts, Montreal (333)

James Wilson Morrice 1865–1924

34 The Ferry, Quebec

c.1909   24 × 32 in. (61 × 81.3 cm.)

Inscription:
Signed l.l., *J. W. Morrice*

Provenance:
André Schoeller, Paris (1927); W. Scott & Sons, Montreal (1932); bought by National Gallery of Canada from W. Scott & Sons, 1938.

Literature:
Donald W. Buchanan, "James Wilson Morrice," *University of Toronto Quarterly,* v, no. 2, January 1936, pl. ii; Donald W. Buchanan, *James Wilson Morrice,* Toronto, Ryerson Press, 1936, pp. 156–7, pl. xv; NGC, *AR,* 1937–8, p. 12, repr.; Donald W. Buchanan, "The Story of Canadian Art," *Canadian Geographical Journal,* xvii, no. 6, December 1938, repr. p. 278; Graham McInnes, *A Short History of Canadian Art,* Toronto, Macmillan, 1939, repr. opp. p. 50; Regina Shoolman and Charles E. Slatkin, *The Enjoyment of Art in America,* Philadelphia and New York, Lippincott, 1942, pl. 709; Graham McInnes, "The Canadian Artist and his Country," *Geographical Journal,* xvi, no. 8, December 1943, repr. p. 399; *CA,* ii, no. 2, December 1944–January 1945, repr. in color p. 54; *Buchanan 1945,* p. 9, pl. i (color); John Lyman, *Morrice,* Montreal, L'Arbre, 1945, pp. 25, 31, pl. 14; Donald W. Buchanan, *James Wilson Morrice,* Toronto, Ryerson Press, 1947, repr. p. 15 (color); A. Y. Jackson, "The Development of Canadian Art," *Journal, Royal Society of Arts,* xcvii, no. 4786, January 1949, repr. p. 132; Graham McInnes, *Canadian Art,* Toronto, Macmillan, 1950, repr. in color opp. p. 84; *The Arts in Canada 1957,* repr. in color p. 70; *Morisset 1960,* repr. in color opp. p. 128; *NGC Cat. 1960,* p. 224, repr.; *Hubbard 1963,* p. 84, pl. 139 (color); Kathleen Daly Pepper, *James Wilson Morrice,* Toronto, Clarke-Irwin, 1966, p. 85, repr. in color pp. 54–5; *Mellen 1970,* repr. p. 71.

Exhibitions:
?Paris, Société Nationale des Beaux-arts, 1909; ?Paris, Salon d'Automne, 1924, *Morrice; Paris 1927,* no. 61; Montreal, W. Scott & Sons, 1932, *James Wilson Morrice,* no. 20; *Imp. Econ. Conf. 1932,* no. 27; NGC, 1937, *James Wilson Morrice,* no. 112, repr.; *Tate 1938,* no. 162, repr.; *Yale 1944; DPC 1945,* no. 111, repr.; *Richmond 1949,* no. 54; *Boston 1949,* no. 66; *AGT 1949,* no. 10, repr.; *Washington 1950,* no. 60, repr.; *Coronation 1953,* no. 51; Venice, xxix Biennale, 1958, Canada, no. 11; Vancouver, Vancouver Art Gallery, 1959, *The Arts in French Canada,* no. 184; *Mexico 1960,* no. 102, repr.; *Bordeaux 1962,* no. 50; MMFA, 1965–6, *J. W. Morrice,* no. 21, repr.; *Vancouver 1966,* no. 58, repr.; *300 Years 1967,* no. 180, repr.; Bath, Holburne Museum, 1968, *James Wilson Morrice,* no. 24, repr.; Bordeaux, Musée de Bordeaux, 1968, *James Wilson Morrice,* no. 24, repr.

A study (7 × 10 in.) for the composition is in the collection of Mrs. G. H. Henderson, Halifax. The view is across the St. Lawrence from Lévis to Quebec.

The National Gallery of Canada, Ottawa (4301)

Maurice Cullen 1866–1934

35 Logging in Winter, Beaupré

1896   25 1/4 × 31 1/2 in. (64.1 × 80 cm.)

Inscription:
Signed and dated l.r., *MAURICE CULLEN 96.*

Provenance:
Mrs. Freda E. Harris, Charlottetown; gift to Art
Gallery of Hamilton from the Women's Commit-
tee, 1956.

Literature:
Art Gallery of Hamilton, *Handbook,* Hamilton,
1954, repr. p. 10; *Kilbourn 1966,* p. 18, repr. in
color p. 17; *Mellen 1970,* p. 6, repr. in color p. 7.

Exhibitions:
Hamilton, Art Gallery of Hamilton, 1956,
Maurice Cullen, no. 10, repr.

The subject is from the "Beaupré Coast," on the
north shore of the St. Lawrence a little below
Quebec.

Art Gallery of Hamilton, Hamilton (56–56–V)

Ludger Larose 1868–1915

36 Saint-Faustin

1899   17 3/4 × 31 3/4 in. (45.1 × 80.7 cm.)

Inscription:
Signed and dated on verso, *L. Larose St-Faustin 1899.*

Provenance:
Dominion Gallery, Montreal; bought by Musée de la Province de Québec, 1949.

Literature:
Hubbard 1957, p. 122; *Morisset 1960,* p. 181, repr. after p. 144; *Hubbard 1960,* pl. 73; *Ostiguy 1971,* p. 17, pl. 27.

Exhibitions:
Coronation 1953, no. 35; *Mexico 1960,* no. 107; *300 Years 1967,* no. 167, repr.

Saint-Faustin is a village in Terrebonne County, Quebec.

Musée du Québec, Quebec (A49 87P)

37 Le camp sur la colline

1909   23 × 28 3/4 in. (58.4 × 73 cm.)

Inscription:
Signed and dated l.l., *A. Suzor-Coté / 1909.*

Provenance:
Bought by National Gallery of Canada from the
Royal Canadian Academy exhibition, 1909.

Literature:
Eric Brown, "Landscape Art in Canada," in
Charles Holme, ed., *Art of the British Empire
Overseas,* London, The Studio, 1917, repr. p. 31;
Robson 1932, repr. in color p. 77; *NGC Cat. 1960,*
p. 288, repr.; *Hubbard 1963,* p. 81, pl. 134;
Hugues de Jouvancourt, "Aurèle de Foy Suzor-
Côté," *VdA,* no. 37, Winter 1964–5, repr. p. 19;
Hugues de Jouvancourt, *Suzor-Côté,* Montreal,
La Frégate, 1967, repr. p. 85; *Mellen 1970,* p. 8,
repr.

Exhibitions:
RCA, 1909, no. 32; *Paris 1927,* no. 222; *Buenos
Aires 1931;* NGC, 1935, *Selected Artists,* no. 99;
AGT, 1937, *Senior Painters in Canada,* no. 76;
Victoria, Art Gallery of Victoria, 1958, *Two
Hundred Years of Canadian Painting,* no. 9.

The subject was probably sketched at the
artist's birthplace, Arthabaska, Quebec.

The English title of the picture is *Settlement on
the Hill-side.*

The National Gallery of Canada, Ottawa (127)

Emily Carr 1871–1945

38   Old-time Coast Village

c.1928   35 3/4 × 50 1/2 in. (90.8 × 128.2 cm.)

Inscription:
Signed l.l., *M. EMILY CARR.*

Provenance:
Emily Carr Trust Collection (1945).

Literature:
Harper 1966, p. 279.

Exhibitions:
AGT, 1945, *Emily Carr,* no. 38; Vancouver, Vancouver Art Gallery, 1971, *Emily Carr,* no. 58,
repr. in color.

The subject is probably from Vancouver Island.

Vancouver Art Gallery, Vancouver (42.3.4)

39 A Rushing Sea of Undergrowth

c.1932–4   44 × 27 in. (111.8 × 68.6 cm.)

Inscription:
Signed l.l., *EMILY CARR.*

Provenance:
Emily Carr Trust Collection (1945).

Literature:
Graham McInnes, "The Canadian Artist and His
Country," *Geographical Journal,* XVI, no. 8, De-
cember 1943, repr. p. 401; *Hubbard 1960,* pl. 99;
Emily Carr, *Hundreds and Thousands,* Toronto,
Clarke-Irwin, 1966, repr. in color opp. p. 134
(opp. p. 126 in deluxe ed.).

Exhibitions:
AGT, 1939, *Canadian Group of Painters;* New
York, World's Fair, 1939, *Canadian Group of
Painters,* no. 10; AGT, 1945, *Emily Carr,* no. 66,
repr.; Vancouver, Vancouver Art Gallery, 1958,
100 Years of B. C. Art, no. 293; *300 Years 1967,*
no. 245, repr.; Vancouver, Vancouver Art
Gallery, 1971, *Emily Carr,* no. 84, repr.

The subject is probably from Vancouver Island.

Vancouver Art Gallery, Vancouver (42.3.17)

Emily Carr 1871–1945

40 British Columbia Forest

c.1932–4   Oil on paper mounted on panel,
36 × 24 in. (91.4 × 61 cm.)

Inscription:
Signed l.r., *M. E. CARR.*

Provenance:
Estate of the artist (1945); bought by Dominion
Gallery, Montreal.

Literature:
Emily Carr, *Hundreds and Thousands,* Toronto,
Clarke-Irwin, 1966, repr. in color opp. p. 134
(opp. p. 200 in deluxe ed.).

Exhibitions:
Edmonton, Edmonton Art Gallery (on loan
1972).

The subject is probably from Vancouver Island.

Dr. and Mrs. Max Stern, Dominion Gallery,
Montreal

J. E. H. MacDonald 1873–1932

41 The Solemn Land

1920   48 × 60 in. (122 × 152 cm.)

Inscription:
Signed and dated l.l., *J. E. H. MacDonald '21.*

Provenance:
Bought by National Gallery of Canada from Ontario Society of Artists exhibition, 1921.

Literature:
NGC, *AR,* 1920–1, p. 12; "Fine Arts from Canada," *Canadian Magazine,* LXIII, no. 3, July 1924, repr. p. 135; Newton MacTavish, *The Fine Arts in Canada,* Toronto, Macmillan, 1925, repr. opp. p. 158; Eric Brown, "La jeune peinture canadienne," *L'Art et les artistes,* new ser., XXI, no. 75, March 1927, repr. opp. p. 186; *Robson 1932,* p. 138, repr.; "Canada Holds its Largest and Best Annual Exhibition at Ottawa," *Art Digest,* VII, no. 12, March 15, 1933, repr. p. 5; A. H. Robson, *J. E. H. MacDonald,* Toronto, Ryerson Press, 1937, p. 7, pl. iv (color); E. R. Hunter, *J. E. H. MacDonald,* Toronto, Ryerson Press, 1940, pp. 26, 53, pl. 8; Graham McInnes, *A Short History of Canadian Art,* Toronto, Macmillan, 1940, p. 26, repr.; Regina Shoolman and Charles E. Slatkin, *The Enjoyment of Art in America,* Philadelphia and New York, Lippincott, 1942, p. 694, pl. 711; *Colgate 1943,* pp. 97, 100; *Buchanan 1945,* pp. 11, 18, pl. 34; Donald W. Buchanan, "J. E. H. MacDonald, Painter of the Forest," *Canadian Geographical Journal,* XXXIII, no. 3, September 1946, repr. p. 149; *NGC Cat. 1960,* p. 190, repr.; J. Russell Harper, "Tour de l'horizon de l'art canadien," *VdA,* no. 26, Spring 1960, repr. p. 34; *Hubbard 1963,* p. 93, pl. 158; *Mellen 1970,* p. 140, repr. in color p. 141.

Exhibitions:
OSA, 1921, no. 107, repr.; *London 1924,* no. 145, repr. (repr. in "Portfolio"); Boston, Art Club, 1926, *Ontario Society of Artists,* no. 26; GS, 1926, no. 90; Philadelphia, Sesqui-centennial International Exposition, 1926, no. 1567, repr.; RCA, 1927, no. 135; AGT, 1933, *J. E. H. MacDonald,* no. 129; NGC, 1933, *James E. H. MacDonald,* no. 3; *GS 1936,* no. 151; London, Ont., Public Library and Art Museum, 1942, *Milestones of Canadian Art,* no. 45; Hamilton, Art Gallery of Hamilton, 1953, *Inaugural Exhibition,* no. 35; *GS 1954,* no. 57, repr.; Victoria, Art Gallery of Victoria, 1958, *Two Hundred Years of Canadian Painting,* no. 13, repr.; AGO, 1965, *J. E. H. MacDonald,* no. 34, repr. in color; *300 Years 1967,* no. 216, repr.

The picture was painted from sketches made on the Montreal River, Algoma District, Ontario, and with the help of a photograph taken of the scene under the artist's supervision.

The National Gallery of Canada, Ottawa (1785)

42   October Shower Gleam

1920   8 1/2 × 10 1/2 in. (21.6 x 26.7 cm.)

Provenance:
Bought from the artist by H. O. McCurry
(Director of the National Gallery of Canada).

Literature:
E. R. Hunter, *J. E. H. MacDonald,* Toronto,
Ryerson Press, 1940, p. 53; *Mellen 1970,* p. 88,
repr. in color.

Exhibitions:
AGT, 1965, *J. E. H. MacDonald,* no. 89, repr.

An Algoma subject, the sketch for the canvas of
1922 in Hart House, University of Toronto.

Mrs. H. O. McCurry, Ottawa

J. E. H. MacDonald 1873–1932

43 Sea-shore, Nova Scotia

1923   28 × 36 in. (71.1 × 91.5 cm.)

Inscription:
Signed and dated l.l., *J. E. H. MacDonald '23.*

Provenance:
Bought by National Gallery of Canada from Ontario Society of Artists exhibition, 1923.

Literature:
E. R. Hunter, *J. E. H. MacDonald,* Toronto, Ryerson Press, 1940, pp. 32, 54–5; *Canadian Review of Music and Art,* I, no. 5, June 1942, repr. p. 11; *Colgate 1943,* p. 100; *NGC Cat. 1960,* p. 191, repr.; NGC, *Engagement Calendar,* Ottawa, 1964, pl. 13 (color).

Exhibitions:
OSA, 1923, no. 131, repr.; *London 1924,* no. 146; *Paris 1927,* no. 128 (as in Art Gallery of Toronto); AGT, 1933, *J. E. H. MacDonald,* no. 132; NGC, 1933, *James E. H. MacDonald,* no. 4; Toronto, Mellors-Laing Gallery, 1937, *J. E. H. MacDonald,* no. 59; NGC travelling exhibition, Ceylon, Pakistan and India, 1954–5, *Canadian Painting,* no. 23; Hamilton, Art Gallery of Hamilton, 1957, *J. E. H. MacDonald,* no. 28; AGO, 1965, *J. E. H. MacDonald,* no. 41, repr.; Victoria, Art Gallery of Victoria, 1967, *Ten Canadians—Ten Decades,* no. 28; *GS 1970,* no. 136, repr.

The subject is from Green Bay or Crescent Beach, near Petite Rivière, Nova Scotia.

The National Gallery of Canada, Ottawa (2914)

44 Little Turtle Lake

1923–5   19 1/2 × 29 3/4 in. (49.5 × 75.5 cm.)

Provenance:
Thoreau MacDonald, Toronto; Dominion Gallery, Montreal (1947); bought by Dr. G. R. McCall.

Literature:
E. R. Hunter, *J. E. H. MacDonald,* Toronto, Ryerson Press, 1940, p. 55; *Hubbard 1957,* pl. xa; *Hubbard 1960,* pl. 89; *Hubbard 1963,* p. 94; *Ostiguy 1971,* p. 32.

Exhibitions:
Montreal, Dominion Gallery, 1947, *J. E. H. MacDonald,* no. 29; *Coronation 1953,* no. 43, repr.; *Mexico 1960,* no. 113; *300 Years 1967,* no. 223, repr.

Turtle Lake is on the Gull River, north-west of Peterborough, Ontario.

Dr. and Mrs. G. R. McCall, Montreal

Tom Thomson 1877–1917

45   Red Leaves

c.1914   Panel
8 1/2 × 10 1/2 in. (21.6 × 26.7 cm.)

Inscription:
Studio stamp l.r. and on verso.

Provenance:
Dr. J. M. MacCallum, Toronto; bequest of Dr.
MacCallum to National Gallery of Canada,
1944.

Literature:
NGC, *AR,* 1945–6, p. 16; *NGC Cat. 1960,* p. 300,
repr.; R. H. Hubbard, *Tom Thomson,* Toronto,
McClelland and Stewart, 1962, pl. 21 (color);
Mellen 1970, p. 70, repr. in color p. 41.

Exhibitions:
NGC travelling exhibition, 1966–7, *Tom Thomson Sketches;* Stratford, Ont., Rothman's Gallery, 1967, *Ten Decades,* no. 22; Owen Sound,
Ont., Tom Thomson Memorial Gallery, 1969,
Paintings by Tom Thomson, no. 12; NGC, 1969,
MacCallum-Jackman Donations, no. 72; AGO,
1971, *The Art of Tom Thomson,* no. 22, repr.

Painted in Algonquin Park, Ontario, probably in
1914. The location was possibly below Tea Lake
Dam (see no. 46) where in 1914 Thomson and
A. Y. Jackson painted together, and where Jackson made a sketch for "The Red Maple" (no. 61).

The National Gallery of Canada, Ottawa (4654)

46 Tea Lake Dam

1915   Panel
8 1/2 × 10 1/2 in. (21.6 × 26.7 cm.)

Inscription:
Studio stamp l.r.; inscribed on verso, *NG/Tea
Lake Dam 1915.*

Provenance:
Tom Thomson estate; bought by National Gallery of Canada through Dr. J. M. MacCallum, Toronto, 1918.

Literature:
Buchanan 1950, pl. iv (color); *NGC Cat. 1960,*
p. 295, repr.; R. H. Hubbard, *Tom Thomson,*
Toronto, McClelland and Stewart, 1962, pl. 26;
Harper 1962, repr. in color p. 430; Ottelyn Addison and Elizabeth Harwood, *Tom Thomson,
the Algonquin Years,* Toronto, Ryerson Press,
1969, repr. in color on dust jacket.

Exhibitions:
NGC, 1922, *Pictures and Sketches by Tom
Thomson* (no. cat. numbers; one of 25 sketches
included); Kitchener, Ont., Kitchener-Waterloo
Art Gallery, 1956, *Tom Thomson,* no. 24; London, Ont., Public Library and Art Museum, 1957,
Tom Thomson, no. 29; Windsor, Ont., Willistead
Art Gallery, 1957, *Tom Thomson,* no. 33; Los
Angeles, County Museum, 1958, *Tom Thomson;*
Owen Sound, Ont., Tom Thomson Memorial
Gallery, 1969, *Paintings by Tom Thomson,* no. 8;
GS 1970, no. 59, repr.; AGO, 1971, *The Art of
Tom Thomson,* no. 69, repr.

Painted in Algonquin Park, Ontario.

The National Gallery of Canada, Ottawa (1523)

Tom Thomson 1877–1917

47 Sunset

c.1915 Panel
8 1/2 × 10 1/2 in. (21.6 × 26.7 cm.)

Inscription:
Studio stamp l.r., and on verso; inscribed on a
label verso, *Sunset.*

Provenance:
Dr. J. M. MacCallum, Toronto; bequest of Dr.
MacCallum to National Gallery of Canada,
1944.

Literature:
NGC, *AR,* 1945–6, p. 16; *NGC Cat. 1960,* p. 307;
R. H. Hubbard, *Tom Thomson,* Toronto, McClelland and Stewart, 1962, pl. 30 (color); *Hubbard
1963,* p. 88; *Mellen 1970,* repr. in color p. 55.

Exhibitions:
NGC travelling exhibition, 1955, *Tom Thomson
Sketches;* London, Ont., Public Library and Art
Museum, 1957, *Tom Thomson;* Windsor, Ont.,
Willistead Art Gallery, 1957, *Tom Thomson,* no.
31; Los Angeles, County Museum, 1958, *Tom
Thomson Sketches;* NGC, 1969, *MacCallum-
Jackman Donations,* no. 91; AGO, 1971, *The Art
of Tom Thomson,* no. 65, repr.

Painted in Algonquin Park, Ontario, probably in
1915.

The National Gallery of Canada, Ottawa (4701)

48 Moose at Night

1916   Panel
8 1/2 × 10 1/2 in. (21.6 × 26.7 cm.)

Inscription:
Studio stamp l.r.; inscribed on verso, *NG Winter 1916 at Studio. J. M. Tom Thomson.*

Provenance:
Tom Thomson estate; bought by National Gallery of Canada through Dr. J. M. MacCallum, Toronto, 1918.

Literature:
Arthur Lismer, "Tom Thomson, 1877–1917," *CA,* v, no. 2, Christmas–New Year 1947–8, repr. p. 61; *NGC Cat. 1960,* p. 298, repr.; *Hubbard 1960,* pl. 92; R. H. Hubbard, *Tom Thomson,* Toronto, McClelland and Stewart, 1962, pl. i (color); *Hubbard 1963,* p. 88; *Kilbourn 1966,* p. 40, repr. in color; *Mellen 1970,* p. 53, repr. in color p. 54.

Exhibitions:
NGC, 1922, *Pictures and Sketches by Tom Thomson* (no. cat. numbers; one of 25 sketches included); NGC travelling exhibition, 1955, *Tom Thomson Sketches;* Windsor, Ont., Willistead Art Gallery, 1957, *Tom Thomson,* no. 24; NGC travelling exhibition, 1966, *Tom Thomson Sketches; 300 Years 1967,* no. 197, repr.; AGO, 1971, *The Art of Tom Thomson,* no. 96, repr.

Painted in Algonquin Park, Ontario, possibly on a trip up the Petawawa Gorges in August 1916.

The National Gallery of Canada, Ottawa (1544)

49 Autumn's Garland

1916–7   48 × 52 in. (122 × 132.1 cm.)

Provenance:
Tom Thomson estate; bought by National Gallery of Canada through Dr. J. M. MacCallum, Toronto, 1918.

Literature:
NGC Cat. 1960, p. 293, repr.; R. H. Hubbard, *Tom Thomson,* Toronto, McClelland and Stewart, 1962, p. 11; *Hubbard 1963,* p. 89; Ottelyn Addison and Elizabeth Harwood, *Tom Thomson, the Algonquin Years,* Toronto, Ryerson Press, 1969, p. 76.

Exhibitions:
US Tour 1918, no. 33; AGT, 1920, *Tom Thomson,* no. 3; NGC, 1922, *Pictures and Sketches by Tom Thomson* (no cat. numbers); *Paris 1927,* no. 238; *Imp. Econ. Conf. 1932,* no. 4; Owen Sound, Ont., Tom Thomson Memorial Gallery, 1967, *Tom Thomson and the Group of Seven,* no. 2; AGO, 1971, *The Art of Tom Thomson,* no. 107, repr.

Painted in Toronto in the winter of 1916–7 from a sketch made in Algonquin Park, Ontario, probably in 1916 (cf. a sketch of the subject, in the collection of M. A. Cowper-Smith, Byron, Ontario, exhibited at Windsor, Ont., Willistead Art Gallery, 1957, *Tom Thomson,* no. 48). The present title of the picture was perhaps given by Dr. MacCallum; Thomson once called it "The Woodland Garland." The composition recalls a poem by Wilfred Campbell, "Autumn"; which includes the phrase, "a crimson clinging vine."

The National Gallery of Canada, Ottawa (1520)

Tom Thomson 1877–1917

50   The Pointers

1916–7   40 × 45 1/2 in. (101.6 × 115 cm.)

Provenance:
Tom Thomson estate; bought by the House Committee of Hart House, with the Print Fund, 1928–9.

Literature:
Blodwen Davies, *A Study of Tom Thomson,* Toronto, Discus Press, 1935, p. 112; A. H. Robson, *Tom Thomson,* Toronto, Ryerson Press, 1937, repr. in color p. 9; *Buchanan 1945,* pl. 38 (as c.1915); Donald W. Buchanan, "The Hart House Collection," *CA,* v, no. 2, Christmas–New Year 1947–8, p. 66, repr. in color p. 63; J. Russell Harper, *Canadian Paintings in Hart House,* Toronto, University of Toronto Press, 1955, pp. 21, 90, repr. in color p. 21; *Hubbard 1960,* pl. 93 (color); R. H. Hubbard, *Tom Thomson,* Toronto, McClelland and Stewart, 1962, p. 12, a detail repr. in color on cover; *Hubbard 1963,* p. 282, pl. 251 (color); Jeremy Adamson, *The Hart House Collection of Canadian Painting,* Toronto, University of Toronto Press, 1969, pp. 11, 141, repr. in color.

Exhibitions:
AGT, 1920, *Tom Thomson,* no. 25; NGC, 1922, *Pictures and Sketches by Tom Thomson* (no cat. numbers); *London 1925; Imp. Econ. Conf. 1932,* no. 8; *Tate 1938,* no. 207, repr. (as "Pageant of the North"); AGT, 1941, *Thomson-Walker Exhibition* (no cat. numbers); *Boston 1949,* no. 91; *Washington 1950,* no. 79; *Coronation 1953,* no. 65, repr.; *GS 1954,* no. 64; Windsor, Ont., Willistead Art Gallery, 1957, *Tom Thomson,* no. 12; *Mexico 1960,* no. 115; *300 Years 1967,* no. 195, repr.; Owen Sound, Ont., Tom Thomson Memorial Gallery, 1969, *Paintings by Tom Thomson,* no. 1; AGO, 1971, *The Art of Tom Thomson,* no. xiii, repr. in color.

Painted in Toronto in the winter of 1916–7 from sketches made in Algonquin Park, Ontario, possibly in 1914 (a related sketch, "Bâteaux," panel 8 1/2 × 10 1/2 in., is in the Art Gallery of Ontario). The picture has also been known as "Pageant of the North." Pointers are long canoes used by lumbermen.

Hart House, University of Toronto

51 The Jack Pine

1916–7   50 1/4 × 55 in. (127.6 × 139.7 cm.)

Provenance:
Tom Thomson estate; bought by National Gallery of Canada through Dr. J. M. MacCallum, Toronto, 1918.

Literature:
H. Mortimer-Lamb, "Studio Talk," *Studio,* LXXVII, no. 317, August 1919, repr. p. 125 (as "The Jack Pine, Lake Couchon [!]"); "Fine Arts from Canada," *Canadian Magazine,* LXIII, no. 3, July 1924, repr. p. 136; Leonard Richmond, "Canadian Art at Wembley," *Studio,* LXXXIX, no. 182, January 1925, repr. in color p. 21; Newton MacTavish, *The Fine Arts in Canada,* Toronto, Macmillan, 1925, repr. opp. p. 150; *Housser 1926,* pp. 120–1; Eric Brown, "La jeune peinture canadienne," *L'Art et les artistes,* new ser., XXI, no. 75, March 1927, repr. p. 192; Blodwen Davies, *Paddle and Palette,* Toronto, Ryerson Press, 1930, repr. p. 23; Blodwen Davies, *A Study of Tom Thomson,* Toronto, Discus Press, 1935, pp. 110–11, repr. in color p. 107; A. H. Robson, *Tom Thomson,* p. 20, repr. in color p. 21; Graham McInnes, "Tom Thomson," *New World Illustrated,* I, March 1940, repr. in color p. 27; *Buchanan 1945,* pl. 43; Audrey Saunders, *Algonquin Story,* Toronto, Department of Lands and Forests, 1947, p. 173; Ray Atherton, "The Man in a Canoe," *CA,* XV, no. 1, January 1958, repr. in color p. 20; *NGC Cat. 1960,* p. 294, repr.; *CA,* XVII, no. 1 (no. 67), January 1960, repr. p. 72; R. H. Hubbard, *Tom Thomson,* Toronto, McClelland and Stewart, 1962, pl. 3 (color); *Hubbard 1963,* p. 89, pl. 154 (color); F. Maud Brown, *Breaking Barriers,* Toronto, Society for Art Publications, 1964, p. 72; *Harper 1966,* p. 282, pl. 249; Blodwen Davies, *Tom Thomson,* Vancouver, Mitchell Press, 1967, p. 76, repr. in color opp. p. 24; Jean Sutherland Boggs, "The National Gallery of Canada," *CA,* XXVI, no. 1, (nos. 128–9), February 1969, repr. p. 4; Ottelyn Addison and Elizabeth Harwood, *Tom Thomson, the Algonquin Years,* Toronto, Ryerson Press, 1969, pp. 54, 59, repr. p. 54; *Boggs 1971,* pl. xxvii (color).

Exhibitions:
US Tour 1918, no. 32; AGT, 1920, *Tom Thomson,* no. 2; NGC, 1922, *Pictures and Sketches by Tom Thomson* (no cat. numbers); *London 1924,* no. 240, repr. (also in "Portfolio"); AGT, 1926, *Inaugural Exhibition,* no. 260; *Paris 1927,* no. 236, repr.; *Imp. Econ. Conf. 1932,* no. 2; *Tate 1938,* no. 213; AGT, 1941, *Thomson-Walker Exhibition* (no cat. numbers); *Boston 1949,* no. 89, repr.; *AGT 1949,* no. 29, repr.; *Washington 1950,* no. 78, repr.; *GS 1954,* no. 65, repr.; Windsor, Willistead Art Gallery, 1957, *Tom Thomson,* no. 9; Los Angeles, County Museum, 1958, *Tom Thomson; 300 Years 1967,* no. 196, repr.; Owen Sound, Ont., Tom Thomson Memorial Gallery, *First Anniversary Exhibition,* no. 6, repr.; *GS 1970,* no. 107, repr.; AGO, 1971, *The Art of Tom Thomson,* no. xv, repr. in color.

The picture was painted in Toronto in the winter of 1916–7 from sketches made in Algonquin Park, Ontario, in 1916—at Lake Cauchon, according to Dr. J. M. MacCallum. A sketch of the subject (8 1/2 × 10 1/2 in.) in a private collection in London, Ont., was exhibited at Windsor, Ont., Willistead Art Gallery, 1957, *Tom Thomson,* no. 40, repr.

The National Gallery of Canada, Ottawa (1519)

Clarence A. Gagnon 1881–1942

52 Crépuscule sur la rive nord

1916?   29 5/8 × 31 3/8 in. (75.3 × 79.7 cm.)

Inscription:
Signed l.l., *Clarence A. Gagnon.*

Provenance:
Bought by National Gallery of Canada, 1925,
from the Royal Canadian Academy Exhibition
of 1924.

Literature:
NGC, *AR,* 1924–5, p. 14; *Buchanan 1945,* pl. 25;
NGC Cat. 1960, p. 98, repr.; Hugues de Jouvan-
court, *Clarence Gagnon,* Montreal, Éditions La
Frégate, 1970, p. 74 (as "Un soir sur la rive
nord").

Exhibitions:
RCA, 1924, no. 62, repr.; AGT, 1926, *French
Canada,* no. 207; Quebec, Musée de la Province
de Québec, 1926, *Gagnon,* no. 207; Quebec,
Musée de la Province de Québec, 1942,
Clarence A. Gagnon, no. 14 (dated 1916); NGC,
1942, *Clarence A. Gagnon,* no. 20; AGT, 1942,
Clarence Gagnon, no. 40; *Richmond 1949,* no.
26; *Boston 1949,* no. 29; *AGT 1949,* no. 23, repr.;
300 Years 1967, no. 191, repr.

Sketched at Baie-Saint-Paul on the lower St.
Lawrence, on the north shore. The subject was
perhaps at least sketched in 1916; a pastel of the
subject (8 1/2 × 10 in.) is in the National Gallery of Canada. The English title of the picture
is *Evening on the North Shore.*

The National Gallery of Canada, Ottawa (3178)

F. H. Varley 1881–1969

53   Squally Weather, Georgian Bay

1920   Panel
11 3/4 × 16 1/4 in. (29.8 × 41.2 cm.)

Inscription:
Signed l.r., *F. H. Varley.*

Provenance:
Gift to National Gallery of Canada from
Mrs. S. J. Williams, Mrs. Harvey Sims, Mrs.
T. R. Cram and Miss Geneva Jackson Kitchener,
Ontario, 1943.

Literature:
Charles Comfort, "Georgian Bay Legacy," *CA,*
VIII, no. 3, Spring 1951, pp. 107–8, repr. (as c.1920);
NGC Cat. 1960, p. 322, repr.

Exhibitions:
Vancouver, Vancouver Art Gallery, 1932, *Varley*
(no cat.); Windsor, Ont., Willistead Art Gallery,
1948, *Group of Seven,* no. 26; AGT, 1954, *F. H.
Varley,* no. 201 (as c.1920); *GS 1954,* no. 79 (as
c.1920); Windsor, Willistead Art Gallery, 1964,
F. H. Varley, no. 7 (as c.1920); *GS 1970,* no. 117,
repr.

This sketch for no. 54 was painted near Dr.
J. M. MacCallum's cottage at Go Home Bay,
Georgian Bay. The pine in the picture is still
standing.

The National Gallery of Canada, Ottawa (4582)

F. H. Varley 1881–1969

54   Stormy Weather, Georgian Bay

c.1920   52 × 64 in. (132.1 × 162.6 cm.)

Inscription:
Signed l.r., *F. H. Varley.*

Provenance:
Bought by National Gallery of Canada from the Group of Seven exhibition, 1921.

Literature:
Housser 1926, p. 214, repr. p. 208; *Robson 1932,* p. 32, repr. in color p. 195; Eric Brown, "Canada's National Painters," *Studio,* CIII, no. 471, June 1932, repr. p. 231; Donald W. Buchanan, "The Story of Canadian Art," *Canadian Geographical Journal,* XVII, no. 6, December 1938, repr. in color p. 291; *Colgate 1943,* frontispiece (color); Graham McInnes, "The Canadian Artist and his Country," *Geographical Journal,* XVI, no. 8, December 1943, repr. p. 403; Thoreau MacDonald, *The Group of Seven,* Toronto, Ryerson Press, 1944, repr. p. 18; *Buchanan 1945,* pl. 69; Graham McInnes, *Canadian Art,* Toronto, Macmillan, 1950, repr. after p. 84; George Elliott, "F. H. Varley—Fifty Years of his Art," *CA,* XII, no. 1, Autumn 1954, repr. in color p. 2; J. A. B. McLeish, *September Gale,* Toronto, Dent, 1955, p. 76; *NGC Cat. 1960,* pp. 320–1, repr.; *Hubbard 1963,* p. 95, pl. 166 (color); *Harper 1966,* p. 295, pl. 269; Barry Lord, "Georgian Bay and the Development of the September Gale Theme in Arthur Lismer's Painting 1912–21," *NGC Bulletin,* V, nos. 1–2, 1967, p. 37, pl. 13; *Mellen 1970,* p. 130, repr. in color; *Boggs 1971,* pl. 131; *Ostiguy 1971,* pl. 88.

Exhibitions:
GS, 1921, no. 54; *London 1924,* no. 252; Boston, Art Club, 1926, *Ontario Society of Artists,* no. 49; *Paris 1927,* no. 239; American Federation of Arts travelling exhibition, 1930, *Contemporary Canadian Artists,* no. 57; *Buenos Aires 1931; GS 1936,* no. 177, repr.; *Yale 1944; Richmond 1949,* no. 74 (as 1921); *Boston 1949,* no. 98; Hamilton, Art Gallery of Hamilton, 1953, *Inaugural Exhibition,* no. 58; AGT, 1954, *F. H. Varley,* no. 10, repr.; *GS 1954,* no. 76; London, Ont., Public Library and Art Museum, 1961, *The Face of Early Canada* (no numbers); Windsor, Ont., Willistead Art Gallery, 1964, *F. H. Varley,* no. 8, repr.; *300 Years 1967,* no. 212, repr.; *GS 1970,* no. 118, repr.

The picture is also known as "Georgian Bay." No. 53 is a sketch for it.

The National Gallery of Canada, Ottawa (1814)

F. H. Varley 1881–1969

55   The Cloud, Red Mountain

c.1928   34 1/4 × 40 1/4 in. (87 × 102.2 cm.)

Inscription:
Signed l.r., *F H VARLEY.*

Provenance:
Bought from the artist by Charles S. Band; bequest of Charles S. Band to Art Gallery of Ontario, 1970.

Literature:
Mellen 1970, p. 171, repr. in color.

Exhibitions:
GS, 1928, no. 60; Buffalo, Albright Art Gallery, 1928, *Canadian Artists,* no. 51; *GS 1936,* no. 191; Ottawa, James Wilson & Co., 1937, *Varley* (no cat.); NGC, 1953, *Collection of Mr. and Mrs. C. S. Band,* no. 43 (as c.1935); AGT, 1954, *F. H. Varley,* no. 16 (as c.1928); Buffalo, Albright Art Gallery, 1958, *Collection of Mr. and Mrs. Charles S. Band,* no. 54; London, Ont., Public Library and Art Museum, 1961, *The Face of Early Canada* (no cat. numbers); Windsor, Ont., Willistead Art Gallery, 1961, *C. S. Band Collection,* no. 24 (as 1939); AGO and MMFA, 1963, *Collection of Mr. and Mrs. Charles S. Band,* no. 38; *GS 1970,* no. 184, repr.

The subject is from the interior of British Columbia.

The Art Gallery of Ontario, Toronto (69/127)

David Milne 1882–1953

56   Winter Carnival, Dominion Square

1924   16 1/8 × 20 1/8 in. (41 × 51.1 cm.)

Inscription:
Signed u.r., *David Milne.*

Provenance:
Douglas M. Duncan, Toronto; gift from the
Douglas M. Duncan Collection to National Gal-
lery of Canada, 1970.

Literature:
NGC, *AR,* 1970-1, p. 79.

Exhibitions:
NGC, 1955, *David Milne,* no. 14; NGC, 1971, *Gift
from the Douglas M. Duncan Collection,* no. 131.

Painted in Montreal, probably in January 1924.
Another version of the subject is in the Agnes
Etherington Art Centre, Queen's University,
Kingston, Ontario.

The National Gallery of Canada, Ottawa (16598)

David Milne 1882–1953

57 Rocks and Dark Pool

c.1928?   18 × 22 in. (45.7 × 55.8 cm.)

Inscription:
Signed l.r., *David Milne.*

Provenance:
Vincent Massey, Port Hope, Ontario; bought by
National Gallery of Canada from Laing Galler-
ies, Toronto, 1959.

Literature:
NGC, *AR,* 1959–60, p. 59, repr.

Probably painted at Lake Timagami in 1928, as
the second of two versions of the subject.
"Rocks in a Wood" (NGC 15517) is probably the
other version.

The National Gallery of Canada, Ottawa (7153)

David Milne 1882–1953

58   Ontario Village

c.1929–33   20 × 26 in. (50.8 × 66 cm.)

Inscription:
Signed l.r., *David Milne.*

Provenance:
Mellors Gallery, Toronto (c. 1934); Vincent Massey, Port Hope, Ontario; bequest of the Right Hon. Vincent Massey to National Gallery of Canada, 1968.

Literature:
NGC, *AR,* 1968–9, p. 67.

Exhibitions:
NGC, 1968, *Vincent Massey Bequest: the Canadian Paintings,* no. 87.

Painted at Palgrave, Ontario.

The National Gallery of Canada, Ottawa (15534)

David Milne 1882–1953

59   Bare Rock Begins to Show

1936   20 1/4 × 24 1/4 in. (51.4 × 61.6 cm.)

Inscription:
Signed and dated l.l., *David Milne 1936.*

Provenance:
Alan Jarvis, Toronto (1955); Douglas M. Duncan, Toronto (1969); gift from the Douglas M. Duncan Collection to National Gallery of Canada, 1970.

Literature:
Alan Jarvis, *David Milne,* Toronto, McClelland and Stewart, 1962, pl. 19; NGC, *AR,* 1970–1, p. 78, repr.

Exhibitions:
NGC, 1955, *David Milne,* no. 47, repr.; NGC, 1971, *Gift from the Douglas M. Duncan Collection,* no. 137.

Painted at Six Mile Lake, Severn River, Ontario

The National Gallery of Canada, Ottawa (16426)

A. Y. Jackson 1882–

60   Terre Sauvage

1913   50 × 60 in. (127 × 152.4 cm.)

Inscription:
Signed and dated l.r., *A Y JACKSON/1913.*

Provenance:
Acquired from the artist by National Gallery of
Canada, 1939, in exchange for "Winter After-
noon" (former acc. no. 1124).

Literature:
Housser 1926, p. 91; Thoreau MacDonald, *The
Group of Seven,* Toronto, Ryerson Press, 1944,
repr. p. 17; Charles Comfort, "Georgian Bay
Legacy," *CA,* VIII, no. 3, Spring 1951, p. 107, repr.
p. 109; A. Y. Jackson, *A Painter's Country,*
Toronto, Clarke-Irwin, 1958, pp. 26, 47, 54 (pp.
31, 55–6, 64 in deluxe ed.); *NGC Cat. 1960,* p. 139,
repr.; *Hubbard 1960,* pl. 85; R. H. Hubbard, *Tom
Thomson,* Toronto, McClelland and Stewart,
1962, p. 7; *Hubbard 1963,* p. 99; *Mellen 1970,*
p. 35, repr. in color p. 34, detail p. 35; *Ostiguy
1971,* pp. 28, 36, pl. 80.

Exhibitions:
RCA, 1918, no. 89 (as "The North Country");
GS, 1920, no. 30; US tour, 1921, *The Group of
Seven Canadian Painters,* no. 7; AGT, 1922, *Retrospective Loan . . . Members of the Ontario Society of Artists,* no. 96; GS, 1922, no. 46; *London
1924,* no. 102; New York, Roerich Museum, 1932,
Contemporary Canadian Artists, no. 26; *GS
1936,* no. 123; Windsor, Ont., Willistead Art Gallery, 1948. *Group of Seven,* no. 11; AGT, 1953,
A. Y. Jackson, no. 8; *GS 1954,* no. 36, repr.; NGC
travelling exhibition, 1967–8, *Canadian Painting
1850–1950,* no. 52; *GS 1970,* no. 15, repr.

Sketched near Georgian Bay, this is the first
canvas A. Y. Jackson painted in Toronto (in
Lawren Harris's studio, November–December
1913). Known before 1936 as "The Northland," it
was at one time christened "Mount Ararat" by
J. E. H. MacDonald.

The National Gallery of Canada, Ottawa (4351)

A. Y. Jackson 1882–

61 The Red Maple

1914   31 1/4 × 38 1/4 in. (79.4 × 97.1 cm.)

Inscription:
Signed and dated l.r., *A. Y. JACKSON,/14.*

Provenance:
Bought by National Gallery of Canada from the
Royal Canadian Academy exhibition, 1914.

Literature:
Canada, House of Commons, *Sessional Papers,*
1916, p. 57; Eric Brown, "Studio Talk," *Studio,*
LXIV, no. 265, April 1915, p. 211, repr. p. 209; Eric
Brown, "Landscape Art in Canada," in Charles
Holme, ed., *Art of the British Empire Overseas,*
London, The Studio, 1917, p. 8, repr. p. 20; *Buchanan 1950,* pl. ii (color); A. Y. Jackson, "Recol-
lections on my Seventieth Birthday," *CA,* x, no.
3, Spring 1953, repr. in color p. 94; A. Y. Jackson,
A Painter's Country, Toronto, Clarke-Irwin,
1958, pp. 31–2 (p. 38 in deluxe ed.); *NGC Cat.
1960,* p. 133, repr.; *Hubbard 1963,* p. 99;
F. Maud Brown, *Breaking Barriers,* Toronto, Society for Art Publications, 1964, p. 72; *Kilbourn
1966,* p. 22, repr. in color p. 21; Naomi Jackson
Groves, *A. Y.'s Canada,* Toronto, Clarke-Irwin,
1968, p. 106; *Mellen 1970,* repr. in color p. 42;
Boggs 1971, p. 127.

Exhibitions:
RCA, 1914, no. 110; *US Tour 1918,* no. 13; AGT,
1953, *A. Y. Jackson,* no. 14; London, Ont., Public
Library and Art Museum, 1961, *The Face of
Early Canada* (no cat. numbers); *300 Years 1967,*
no. 186, repr.; *GS 1970,* no. 52, repr.

Sketched below Tea Lake Dam, Algonquin Park,
Ontario, on a sketching trip with Tom Thomson
in the autumn of 1914 (cf. no. 45). A sketch of
the composition is in the McMichael Conservation Collection of Art, Kleinburg, Ontario
(8 1/2 × 10 1/2 in.)

The National Gallery of Canada, Ottawa (1038)

A. Y. Jackson 1882–

62   Night, Pine Island

1921   25 1/2 × 32 in. (64.8 × 81.3 cm.)

Inscription:
Signed l.l., *A. Y. JACKSON.*

Provenance:
Bought from the artist, c.1933, by H. O. McCurry
(then Assistant Director of the National Gallery
of Canada).

Literature:
Mellen 1970, repr. in color p. 124.

Exhibitions:
NGC, *Annual Exhibition,* 1933, no. 134; *Coronation 1953,* no. 27, repr.; *300 Years 1967,* no. 218,
repr. (a detail repr. in color on cover).

Sketched on Georgian Bay in 1920 and painted
in 1921.

Mrs. H. O. McCurry, Ottawa

A. Y. Jackson 1882–

63 Saint-Hilarion

1924?   Panel
8 1/4 × 10 1/2 in. (21 × 26.7 cm.)

Inscription:
Signed l.r., *A. Y. JACKSON.*

Provenance:
Bought by Vincent Massey; bequest of the
Right Hon. Vincent Massey to National Gallery
of Canada, 1968.

Exhibitions:
AGT, 1934, *Collection of Hon. Vincent and Mrs.
Massey,* no. 125; NGC, 1968, *Vincent Massey Be-
quest: the Canadian Paintings,* no. 20, repr.

Saint-Hilarion is a village in the Laurentian
Mountains between Baie-Saint-Paul and Mur-
ray Bay. Jackson visited it early in 1924 (see
A. Y. Jackson, *A Painter's Country,* Toronto,
Clarke-Irwin, 1958, p. 62) and revisited it in sub-
sequent years.

The National Gallery of Canada, Ottawa (15487)

A. Y. Jackson 1882–

64 Northern Lake

c.1928   32 1/2 × 50 in. (82.5 × 127 cm.)

Inscription:
Signed l.l., *A Y JACKSON.*

Provenance:
Bought from the artist, c.1930, by Vincent Massey, Port Hope, Ontario; bequest of the Right Hon. Vincent Massey to National Gallery of Canada, 1968.

Literature:
A. H. Robson, *A. Y. Jackson,* Toronto, Ryerson Press, 1938, p. 28, repr. in color p. 29; Graham McInnes, "A. Y. Jackson," *New World Illustrated,* I, no. 2, April 1940, repr. in color p. 26; A. Y. Jackson, *A Painter's Country,* Toronto, Clarke-Irwin, 1958, p. 104 (p. 125 in deluxe ed.); Naomi Jackson Groves, *A. Y. 's Canada,* Toronto, Clarke-Irwin, 1968, p. 202.

Exhibitions:
AGT, 1933, *Canadian Group of Painters,* no. 38 (as "Frieze of Spruce"); AGT, 1934, *Collection of Hon. Vincent and Mrs. Massey,* no. 117; *Tate 1938,* no. 111; AGT, 1953, *A. Y. Jackson,* no. 45; *GS 1954,* no. 38; NGC, 1968, *Vincent Massey Bequest: the Canadian Paintings,* no. 13, repr.

The picture has wrongly been called "The Collin Range." It was sketched at Walsh Lake (the present Wecho Lake?) in the Yellowknife region, N.W.T. The "November" formerly attached to the title is also incorrect, as the subject was sketched in July 1928. A related drawing, "Yellowknife, Walsh Lake, Evening," is in the McMichael Conservation Collection, Kleinburg, Ontario.

The National Gallery of Canada, Ottawa (15480)

65 A September Gale, Georgian Bay (study)

1920   20 1/8 × 24 in. (51.1 × 61 cm.)

Inscription:
Signed and dated l.l., *A Lismer '20.*

Provenance:
Bought from the artist by Vincent Massey, Port
Hope, Ontario; bequest of the Right Hon. Vincent Massey to National Gallery of Canada,
1968.

Literature:
J. A. B. McLeish, *September Gale,* Toronto,
Dent, 1955, p. 205; Barry Lord, "Georgian Bay
and the Development of the September Gale
Theme in Arthur Lismer's Painting, 1912–21,"
NGC Bulletin, v, nos. 1–2, 1967, p. 33, repr. p. 36;
NGC, *AR,* 1968–9, p. 65; *Mellen 1970,* p. 65.

Exhibitions:
AGT, 1934, *Collection of Hon. Vincent and Mrs.
Massey,* no. 133 (as "The Lone Pine"); *Washington 1950,* no. 48; AGT, 1950, *Arthur Lismer,* no.
104; NGC, 1968, *Vincent Massey Bequest: the
Canadian Paintings,* no. 26, repr.; *GS 1970,* no.
115, repr.

This is a trial study for the large canvas of 1921
in the National Gallery of Canada. The subject
is from the same location as no. 54.

The National Gallery of Canada, Ottawa (15493)

Arthur Lismer 1885–1969

66 Quebec Village

1925   Board
12 × 16 in. (30.5 × 40.7 cm.)

Provenance:
Bought from the artist by National Gallery of
Canada, 1948.

Literature:
Graham McInnes, "Art of Canada," *Studio,*
CXIV, no. 533, August 1937, repr. p. 66; NGC, *AR,*
1947–8, p. 17; J. A. B. McLeish, *September Gale,*
Toronto, Dent, 1955, p. 178, repr. (as signed and
painted in 1926); A. Y. Jackson, "Arthur
Lismer," *Educational Record of the Province of
Quebec,* LXXI, no. 1, January–March 1955, repr.
p. 12; *NGC Cat. 1960,* p. 178, repr. (as 1926).

Exhibitions:
AGT, 1950, *Arthur Lismer,* no. 109 (as signed
and painted in 1926); *GS 1954,* no. 52 (as 1926);
GS 1970, no. 157, repr.

Painted in 1925 at Saint-Hilarion, Quebec (see
no. 63). Study for the canvas of 1926 in the
Agnes Etherington Art Centre, Kingston, Ontario.

The National Gallery of Canada, Ottawa (4940)

Lawren Harris 1885–1970

67 Shacks

1919   42 × 50 1/4 in. (106.7 × 127.6 cm.)

Inscription:
Signed and dated l.l., *LAWREN/HARRIS/1919.*

Provenance:
Bought by National Gallery of Canada from the
Group of Seven exhibition 1920.

Literature:
NGC, *AR,* 1920-1, p. 12; *Buchanan 1950,* pl. 27;
NGC Cat. 1960, p. 110, repr.; Bess Harris and
R. P. Colgrove, *Lawren Harris,* Toronto, Mac-
millan, 1969, repr. in color p. 31; *Mellen 1970,* pl.
251.

Exhibitions:
OSA, 1919, no. 80(?) (as "Shacks, Lambton");
GS, 1920, no. 20; *London 1924,* no. 86; *GS 1936,*
no. 64; Seattle, University of Washington, 1942,
Lawren Harris; London, Ont., Public Library
and Art Museum, 1946, *Group of Seven,* no. 8;
AGT, 1948. *Lawren Harris,* no. 7 (as dated 1917);
GS 1954, no. 26 (as dated 1917); *Mexico 1960,* no.
130; NGC, 1963, *Lawren Harris,* no. 12; Sarnia,
Ont., Public Library and Art Gallery, 1966,
Group of Seven; GS 1970, no. 106, repr.

Painted on the outskirts of Toronto (Lambton is
one of the western suburbs).

The National Gallery of Canada, Ottawa (1693)

68 Lake Superior

c.1924   40 1/4 × 50 1/8 in. (102.2 × 127.3 cm.)

Provenance:
Bought from the artist by Charles S. Band, Toronto; bequest of Charles S. Band to Art Gallery of Ontario, 1970.

Literature:
Paul Duval, "Lawren Harris's Switch to Abstract Art," *Saturday Night,* LXIV, no. 1, October 9, 1948, repr. p. 2; Northrop Frye, "The Pursuit of Form," *CA,* VI, no. 2, Christmas 1948, repr. p. 57; *Hubbard 1957,* pl. xb; *Hubbard 1960,* pl. 88; Charles S. Band, "The Private Collector," *CA,* XVIII, no. 3, May–June 1961, repr. p. 161; *Hubbard 1963,* p. 102, pl. 171.

Exhibitions:
GS, 1926, no. 20(?); Buffalo, Albright Art Gallery, 1928, *Canadian Artists* (one of nos. 16–18: "Lake Superior" I, II, III); New York, Roerich Museum, 1932, *Contemporary Canadian Artists,* no. 18; NGC, 1933, *Annual Exhibition,* no. 94(?); Atlantic City, Heinz Art Salon, 1933, *Canadian Group of Painters,* no. 15, repr.; *GS 1936,* no. 74(?); AGT, 1948, *Lawren Harris,* no. 34, repr.; NGC, 1953, *Collection of Mr. and Mrs. C. S. Band,* no. 13, repr.; *Coronation 1953,* no. 24; Buffalo, Albright Art Gallery, 1958, *Collection of Mr. and Mrs. Charles S. Band,* no. 13, repr.; Vancouver, Vancouver Art Gallery, 1960, *Collection of Mr. and Mrs. Charles S. Band,* no. 13; Windsor, Ont., Willistead Art Gallery, 1961, *C. S. Band Collection,* no. 11; AGO and MMFA, 1963, *Collection of Mr. and Mrs. Charles S. Band,* no. 17, repr. (as signed and dated 1922); Port Arthur, Ont., Lakehead College, 1964, *The Group of Seven and Lake Superior,* no. 11; *300 Years 1967,* no. 220, repr. in color (as signed and dated 1922); *GS 1970,* no. 145, repr.

A sketch (12 × 15 in.) for the composition is at Canada Packers Ltd., Toronto.

The Art Gallery of Ontario, Toronto (69/121)

69 Maligne Lake, Jasper Park

1924 48 × 60 in. (121.9 × 152.4 cm.)

Inscription:
Signed and dated l.l., *LAWREN/HARRIS/1924.*

Provenance:
Bought by National Gallery of Canada from the
National Gallery Annual Exhibition, 1928.

Literature:
Housser 1926, p. 197; NGC, *AR,* 1927–8, p. 20;
Stewart Dick, "Canadian Landscape of Today,"
Apollo, xv, no. 90, June 1932, repr. p. 281; Gra-
ham McInnes, "The Canadian Artist and his
Country," *Geographical Magazine,* xvi, no. 8,
December 1943, repr. p. 405; *NGC Cat. 1960,*
p. 111, repr.; Bess Harris and R. G. P. Colgrove,
Lawren Harris, Toronto, Macmillan, 1969, repr.
in color p. 19.

Exhibitions:
GS, 1925, no. 20; *London 1925; Paris 1927,* no.
60; NGC, 1928, *Annual Exhibition,* no. 63;
Buenos Aires 1931; Seattle, University of Wash-
ington, 1942, *Lawren Harris;* AGT, 1948, *Lawren
Harris,* no. 33; London, Ont., Public Library and
Art Museum, 1949, *Lawren Harris; Boston 1949,*
no. 33, repr.; *GS 1954,* no. 25, repr.; NGC, 1963,
Lawren Harris, no. 38; Windsor, Ont., Willistead
Art Gallery, and London, Ont., Public Library
and Art Museum, 1969, *Approaches to Land-
scape Painting,* no. 11; *GS 1970,* no. 152, repr.

A sketch for the composition (10 3/4 × 13 3/4
in.) is in the collection of S. C. Torno, Toronto,
and a drawing after the composition is in the
National Gallery of Canada. A rendering in tem-
pera, prepared for silk-screen reproduction, is in
the McMichael Conservation Collection, Kleinburg, Ontario.

The National Gallery of Canada, Ottawa (3541)

Lawren Harris 1885–1970

70 North Shore, Baffin Island

1930   Board
11 7/8 × 14 3/4 in. (30.2 × 37.5 cm.)

Provenance:
Bought by National Gallery of Canada from
Laing Galleries, Toronto, 1942.

Literature:
NGC Cat. 1960, p. 112.

Exhibitions:
AGT, 1948, *Lawren Harris,* no. 138; St. John's,
Nfld., Memorial University, and Bermuda Soci-
ety of Arts, 1961, *Canadian Paintings.*

The National Gallery of Canada, Ottawa (4561)

71 Isolation Peak

1929   42 × 50 in. (106.7 × 127 cm.)

Provenance:
Bought from the artist by Hart House with income from the Harold and Murray Wrong Memorial Fund, 1946.

Literature:
"Lawren Harris," *Mayfair,* XXII, no. 10, November 1948, repr. p. 74 (as 1931); Northrop Frye, "The Pursuit of Form," *CA*, VI, no. 2, Christmas 1948, repr. p. 55; J. Russell Harper, *Canadian Paintings in Hart House,* Toronto, University of Toronto Press, 1955, p. 87, repr. p. 34; Jeremy Adamson, *The Hart House Collection of Canadian Paintings,* Toronto, University of Toronto Press, 1969, p. 92, repr. p. 44; Bess Harris and R. P. Colgrove, *Lawren Harris,* Toronto, Macmillan, 1969, repr. in color p. 73 (as 1931); *Mellen 1970,* p. 161, repr.

Exhibitions:
American Federation of Arts travelling exhibition, 1930, *Contemporary Canadian Artists,* no. 18; *GS, 1931, no. 63; NGC, 1932, Annual Exhibition,* no. 98; Rio de Janeiro, Museu Nacional de Belas Artes, 1944, *Pintura canadense contemporanea,* no. 81; AGT, 1948, *Lawren Harris,* no. 53, repr.; NGC, 1963, *Lawren Harris,* no. 37 (as 1931); *GS 1970,* no. 187, repr.

A sketch for the composition is in the collection of James Broughton, Vancouver. A related sketch (11 3/4 × 14 3/4 in.) is in the collection of S. C. Torno, Toronto. The title probably refers to Isolated Peak in the Kootenay District, British Columbia.

Hart House, University of Toronto

F. H. Johnston 1888–1949

72 Near the Berry Patch

c.1918–9?   Board
10 1/2 × 13 in. (26.7 × 33 cm.)

Inscription:
Signed l.r., *Frank H. Johnston.*

Provenance:
Bought by National Gallery of Canada from Dominion Gallery, Montreal, 1958.

Literature:
NGC Cat. 1960, p. 150.

Exhibitions:
Art Institute of Ontario travelling exhibition, 1959–60, *The Group of Seven.*

Painted before 1926, when Johnston began to sign his pictures "Franz Johnston"; probably painted in the Algoma District, Ontario, 1918–19.

The National Gallery of Canada, Ottawa (6940)

Franklin Carmichael 1890–1945

73 Lake Superior

1929   Board
10 × 12 in. (25.4 × 30.5 cm.)

Inscription:
Signed l.l., *FRANK/CARMICHAEL.*

Provenance:
Bought by National Gallery of Canada from
Laing Galleries, Toronto, 1957.

Literature:
NGC Cat. 1960, p. 42.

Exhibitions:
Port Arthur, Ont., Lakehead College, 1964, *The
Group of Seven and Lake Superior,* no. 2; *GS
1970,* no. 169, repr.

Painted in 1929 on the north shore of Lake Superior.

The National Gallery of Canada, Ottawa (6665)

L. L. FitzGerald 1890–1956

74 Doc Snider's House

1931   29 1/2 × 33 1/2 in. (74.9 × 85.1 cm.)

Inscription:
Signed and dated l.l., *L. L. FITZGERALD 1931.*

Provenance:
Gift of P. D. Ross, Ottawa, to National Gallery
of Canada, 1932.

Literature:
NGC, *AR,* 1931–2, pp. 7–8; Eric Brown, "Can-
ada's National Painters," *Studio,* cIII, no. 471,
June 1932, repr. p. 315; "Moderne Malerei in
Kanada," *Die Kunst für Alle,* xLVIII, no. 11, Au-
gust 1933, repr. p. 347; Bertram Brooker, ed.,
Yearbook of the Arts in Canada, Toronto, Mac-
millan, 1936, pl. 1; Graham McInnes, "Art of
Canada," *Studio,* cIV, no. 533, August 1937, repr.
p. 60; *Buchanan 1945,* pl. 80 (as 1930); Ferdinand
Eckhardt, "The Technique of L. L. FitzGerald,"
CA, xv, no. 2 (no. 160), April 1958, repr. in color
p. 116; *NGC Cat. 1960,* p. 84, repr.; *Kilbourn
1966,* p. 71, repr. in color; *Boggs 1971,* pl. 140.

Exhibitions:
GS, 1931, no. 53; NGC, 1932, *Annual Exhibition,*
no. 60; New York, Roerich Museum, 1932, *Contemporary Canadian Painters,* no. 13 (as Vincent
Massey collection); *GS 1936,* no. 44, repr.; NGC
travelling exhibition, Southern Dominions of the
British Empire, 1936, *Contemporary Canadian
Painting,* no. 23, repr.; *Yale 1944; DPC 1945,* no.
165, repr.; *Richmond 1949,* no. 23; *AGT 1949,* no.
46; *GS 1954,* no. 19, repr.; Winnipeg, Winnipeg
Art Gallery, 1958, *L. L. FitzGerald,* no. 7, repr.

Dr. Snider, a dentist, was a neighbor of the artist in Lyle Street, St. James, Winnipeg.

The National Gallery of Canada, Ottawa (3993)

Biographies of Artists

Apart from the monographs noted at the end of some biographies, the main sources of information are J. Russell Harper, *Early Painters and Engravers in Canada,* Toronto, University of Toronto Press, 1970 (for painters born before 1867); Dennis Reid, *The Group of Seven* (exhibition catalogue), Ottawa, National Gallery of Canada, 1970 (for members of the Group of Seven); and numerous literary and documentary sources (see Bibliography) at the National Gallery of Canada (for other artists). Artists mentioned in the biographies and included in this exhibition are marked with an asterisk*. Numbers following the artist's name indicate entries in this catalogue.

Abbreviations:
RCA   Royal Canadian Academician
PRCA   President of the Royal Canadian
        Academy of Arts

William Armstrong 1822–1914 (*20*)

Born in Dublin, the son of a general in the Royal Irish Artillery. Studied art in Dublin and won a prize for architectural drawing. Was an apprentice civil engineer for English and Irish railways before emmigrating to Toronto 1851. Began his visits to the west in 1868 and, as a civil engineer, accompanied General Garnet Wolseley on various Canadian Pacific Railway construction parties and visited the Rocky Mountains with Sir Sandford Fleming's party 1877. Drawing-master at the Toronto Normal School, and later at the Toronto secondary schools for a long period. Painted documentary pictures of Canada mainly in watercolors often for reproduction in the illustrated papers. Nominated a charter RCA 1880 but resigned over the Academy's hanging policy. Died in Toronto.
  Monograph: Henry C. Campbell, *Early Days on the Great Lakes: the Art of William Armstrong,* Toronto, McClelland and Stewart, 1971

Ebenezer Birrell 1801–1888 (*11*)

Born in Scotland and emigrated to Canada 1834, settling near Pickering near Toronto. Became a prominent citizen of his district, serving as president of the Pickering Agricultural Society 1853–9, local superintendent of education 1856–65, lieutenant-colonel of Militia and judge of exhibits in Upper Canada Provincial Exhibitions 1854–5. Painted portraits and landscapes in Canada, and some watercolors of British scenery. Died presumably at Pickering, Ontario.

Franklin Carmichael 1890–1945 (*73*)

Born at Orillia, Ontario. Went to Toronto 1911 and studied at the Ontario College of Art with William Cruikshank and G. A. Reid, and at the Toronto Technical School with Gustav Hahn; also at the Académie Royale, Antwerp, 1913. On his return settled in Toronto and worked at the commercial art firms, Grip Ltd. and Rous & Mann. Original member of the Group of Seven 1920. RCA 1935. Taught at the Ontario College of Art 1932–45. Died in Toronto.

Emily Carr 1871–1945 (*38–40*)

Born in Victoria, British Columbia. Studied at the San Francisco School of Art 1889–94 and at the Westminster School of Art, London, and elsewhere in England 1899–1905. Returned after both periods to teach and to paint the Indian villages on the Pacific coast. Was in Europe 1910–11, studying at the Académie Colarossi, Paris, and traveling for her health in Sweden. Exhibited at the Salon d'Automne, Paris, 1911, and at this time she probably came into contact with the New Zealand painter Frances Hodgkins. On her return to Canada she held her first exhibition in Vancouver and painted the Indian villages in a Fauve style. Returned to Victoria and built her apartment house (the "House of All Sorts") 1913. In the 1920s she made pottery and carpets with Indian designs to make a living. In 1927, at her first exhibition in eastern Canada, she met Lawren Harris* and others of the Group of Seven, who inspired her to develop her characteristic, monumental style. Was probably somewhat influenced by Mark Tobey who first visited her 1928. Disposed of her apartment house 1936 and began to write her autobiographical books *(The House of All Sorts,* etc.*)*. Died in Victoria.

Monograph: Emily Carr, *Hundreds and Thousands, the Journals of Emily Carr,* Toronto, Clarke-Irwin, 1966.

Maurice Galbraith Cullen 1866–1934 *(35)*

Born in St. John's, Newfoundland; the family moved to Montreal 1870. Entered a commercial firm in Montreal 1880 but studied sculpture with Philippe Hébert in his spare time. Went to Paris 1889 and studied at the École des Beaux-Arts until 1892. Became an Impressionist painter and worked at Moret and Giverny. Exhibited at the Salon of 1895, then returned to Canada and painted in Quebec and on the St. Lawrence before opening a studio in Montreal. Painted with Morrice* in Venice 1896–7 and 1902, returning to paint in and around Quebec 1902–8. From 1912 he painted at Lac Tremblant in the Laurentians, where he built a cabin c.1920. RCA 1907. Visited Newfoundland 1911–12. Painted for the Canadian War Memorials 1917–18. Died at Chambly near Montreal.

Thomas Davies c.1737–1812 *(2–5)*

Born at Woolwich, where he entered the Royal Military Academy 1755 and had lessons from its drawing-master Gamaliel Massiot. After his first commission in the Royal Artillery 1756 was sent 1757 to Halifax, where he made the first of his many watercolor records. Accompanied Amherst's Louisbourg and Monckton's St. John River expeditions 1758. Accompanied Amherst's Lake Champlain campaign 1759 and the campaign against Montreal 1760. Explored the St. Lawrence and Lake Ontario 1760–2. In England 1763–4, returning 1764 and painting landscapes

in New York and New Jersey. After a period in England 1767–73 he served in the war of the American Revolution. Was again in England 1779–83, then served at Gibraltar 1783–4. Began his last North American tour of duty 1786, passing through Madeira and the West Indies on his way to Quebec, where he painted his finest series of watercolors. By the time of his final return to England 1790 he was a recognized ornithologist, having been elected Fellow of the Royal Society in 1781. Exhibited at the Royal Academy between 1771 and 1806. Died a lieutenant-general at Blackheath near Woolwich.

Monographs: R. H. Hubbard, *Thomas Davies* (exhibition catalogue), Ottawa, National Gallery of Canada, 1972; R. H. Hubbard, *Thomas Davies in Early Canada,* Ottawa, Oberon Press, 1972.

Aaron Allan Edson 1846–1888 *(29)*

Born at Stanbridge in the Eastern Townships (of Quebec) of American parents who had emigrated to Canada; the family moved to Montreal 1861. Was educated for a business career but turned to painting and studied with Robert S. Duncanson in Montreal. Was in Europe 1864–6 studying under William Holyoake in London and under Léon Pelouse in Paris. On his return he took a studio in Montreal. Founding member of the Society of Canadian Artists, Montreal, 1867 and charter RCA 1880. Exhibited at the Paris Salon 1883 and the Royal Academy, London, 1886. Visited the Rocky Mountains but painted chiefly in the Eastern Townships. Moved 1886 to Glen Sutton, Quebec, where he died.

Lionel LeMoine FitzGerald 1890–1956 *(74)*

Born in Winnipeg and spent the summers in his youth on a farm at Snowflake, Manitoba. Studied at A. S. Kezthelyi's school of art, Winnipeg, then worked for a publishing house and at displays and interior decoration in a department store. Spent a season c.1921 at the Art Students League, New York, studying under Kenneth

Hayes Miller and Boardman Robinson. Taught at the Winnipeg School of Art 1924–49. Member of the Group of Seven in the last year of its existence 1932–3. Visited the Pacific coast several times between 1942 and 1949 and Mexico 1951, but otherwise painted in Manitoba. Died in Winnipeg.

Charles Ramus Forrest active c.1821–3 *(8)*

British army officer and topographical painter. Was in Canada c.1821–3 as aide-de-camp to the Commander of British forces in North America, advancing from captain to lieutenant-colonel. Painted views of Quebec and landscapes of the canoe route to the further Great Lakes.

John Arthur Fraser 1838–1898 *(27–28)*

Born in London, where he studied at the Royal Academy Schools under Francis William Topham and Richard Redgrave. Painted portraits in England before emigrating to Canada c.1856. Worked in the studio of William Notman, the Montreal photographer from c.1860, representing him in Ottawa 1867 and becoming partner in charge of the Toronto branch 1868. Also taught painting. Founding member of the Society of Canadian Artists, Montreal, 1867, of the Ontario Society of Artists, 1872, and charter RCA 1880. Moved to the United States 1883, working in Chicago and Boston but returning briefly to paint in the Rocky Mountains for the Canadian Pacific Railway 1886. Visited England and Scotland 1888. Died in New York.

Clarence Alphonse Gagnon 1881–1942 *(52)*

Born in Montreal (his father was French Canadian, his mother English). Studied at the school of the Art Association of Montreal under William Brymner 1897–1900. First painted at Baie-Saint-Paul on the north shore of the lower St. Lawrence 1900. Went to Paris 1904 and studied at the Académie Julian; was also influenced by Morrice*. Returned to Canada 1909 and thereaf-

ter divided his time between Montreal, Baie-Saint-Paul and Paris. RCA 1922. From 1922 to 1936 he lived mainly in Paris, painting in France and Norway. Made illustrations for several books including Hémon's *Maria Chapdelaine.* Returned finally to Montreal 1936. In 1941 he exhibited a model of a typical Quebec village, which he hoped to develop as an outdoor museum. Died in Montreal.

Monograph: Hugues de Jouvancourt, *Clarence Gagnon,* Montreal, La Frégate, 1970.

Lawren Stewart Harris 1885–1970 *(67–71)*

Born at Brantford, Ontario, the son of a leading farm-implement manufacturer. Had a year at the University of Toronto 1903 but turned to painting and went to Berlin 1904, studying with Adolf Schlabitz and Franz Skarbina. After his return to Canada 1907 he travelled to the Middle East 1907–8 and to lumber camps in Minnesota 1909, illustrating articles in *Harper's Magazine.* Settled in Toronto 1911 and there met (1911) and sketched with (1912) J. E. H. MacDonald*. With MacDonald he visited an exhibition of Scandinavian painting in Buffalo 1913. A leader of the Toronto movement in painting, he encouraged MacDonald and Thomson* to paint full time and with another art patron, Dr. J. M. MacCallum, built the Studio Building for artists 1914. Served in the army 1916–18. Made the famous "box-car" painting trips to Algoma with MacDonald and Johnston* 1918 and with these and Jackson* 1919. Original member of the Group of Seven 1920. Made painting trips to Nova Scotia and Newfoundland 1921, the Rocky Mountains 1924 ff., the lower St. Lawrence 1929, the Arctic 1930 and the Gaspé 1932. Left Toronto 1934 and lived in New England until 1939. After a year (1940) at Santa Fe, as a member of the Transcendental Painting Group, he settled in Vancouver; his later work was abstract. Trustee of the National Gallery of Canada 1950–65. Died in Vancouver.

Monograph: Bess Harris and R. P. Colgrove, *Lawren Harris,* Toronto, Macmillan, 1969.

George Heriot 1766-1844 (6)

Born at Haddington, East Lothian, and was educated at the Edinburgh High School. Entered the Royal Military Academy at Woolwich and had lessons from its drawing-master Paul Sandby. Was stationed in Quebec 1791 and served in the army paymaster's department. Was appointed deputy postmaster-general of British North America 1800 and in pursuance of his duties traveled extensively in the colonies. Resigned his post after a dispute with the Administrator of Quebec, Sir George Drummond, and returned to England. Some of his drawings were engraved 1796, and in 1797 he exhibited two views in Canada at the Royal Academy. Published his *History of Canada* 1804 and his *Travels through the Canadas,* illustrated with aquatints from his drawings, 1807. Died in England.

William George Richardson Hind
1833-1888 (24)

Born at Nottingham, the brother of Henry Youle Hind the explorer. Studied art in London and Europe before emigrating to Canada 1852, apparently to join his brother in Toronto. Drawing-master at the Toronto Normal School 1856. After revisiting England (where he evidently had some contact with the Pre-Raphaelites) he returned to Canada 1861 and accompanied his brother's expedition to Labrador, where he made many sketches. In 1862 he accompanied the Toronto party of the "Overlanders of '62" to the gold fields of the Cariboo in British Columbia, painting incidents of the trip from Fort Garry to Victoria. Also visited San Francisco and the California gold fields. After a period in Victoria 1863-c.1865 he went to his brother's house at Windsor, Nova Scotia. Painted in Nova Scotia and New Brunswick and from 1880 lived principally at Sussex, New Brunswick, where he died.

Alexander Young Jackson 1882- (60-64)

Born in Montreal. In his youth he worked for a lithographing firm, with painting lessons in the evenings from Edmond Dyonnet and William Brymner. Went to Europe 1905 and visited Paris and Rotterdam, then worked at commercial art in Chicago 1906-7, attending evening classes at the Art Institute. In Europe 1907-9, studying at the Académie Julian in Paris and making painting trips to Italy, Belgium and Holland. After returning to Montreal he painted at Sweetsburg, Quebec, and Georgian Bay. Again in Europe 1911-13, visiting France, England and Italy. On his return he sketched at Émileville, Quebec, and on Georgian Bay and was encouraged by Harris* to settle in Toronto. In 1914 he sketched for the first time in Algonquin Park (with Thomson*) and visited the Rocky Mountains. Served in the army from 1915 and painted for the Canadian War Memorials in France 1917-19. On his return settled in Toronto, making continuous sketching trips: to Halifax 1919, Algoma 1918 and 1919 (on the "box-car" trips with Harris*, MacDonald* and Johnston*), the lower St. Lawrence 1921 ff., the Rocky Mountains 1924, British Columbia 1926, the Arctic 1927 ff. and many other places. Original member of the Group of Seven 1920. RCA 1919 (resigned 1933 but re-elected 1953). Invested Companion of the Order of St. Michael and St. George (CMG) 1946. Lived in Ottawa 1955-68 and has since lived at the McMichael Conservation Collection, Kleinburg, Ontario.

Monographs: A. Y. Jackson, *A Painter's Country,* Toronto, Clarke-Irwin, 1958; Naomi Jackson Groves, *A.Y.'s Canada,* Toronto, Clarke-Irwin, 1968.

Otto Reinhold Jacobi 1812-1901 (16)

Born at Königsberg, East Prussia, where he had his first painting lessons. Studied at the Berlin and Düsseldorf academies 1832-5. Commissions for watercolors, which he received from the Empress of Russia and the Grand Duke of Nassau, resulted in his appointment as court painter at Wiesbaden c.1841. Was invited to Canada to paint Shawinigan Falls as a gift to the Prince of Wales during the latter's visit to Canada 1860. Settled in Montreal as a painter and also worked for William Notman the photographer. Accompanied Prince Arthur's party on a trip up the Ottawa 1869. After painting at Ardoch, North Dakota 1877 he settled in Toronto 1878. Charter RCA 1880. Moved to Philadelphia 1882 but returned to Toronto 1891. PRCA 1891–3. Visited the Rocky Mountains. After his wife's death he went to live with a son in the Dakota country. Died at Java, South Dakota.

Francis Hans Johnston 1888–1949 (72)

Born in Toronto, where he studied at the Toronto Technical School under Gustav Hahn and the Central Ontario School of Art under William Cruikshank and G. A. Reid, while working as a commercial artist at Brigden's and later at Grip Ltd. 1911. Went to Philadelphia 1912 and studied at the Pennsylvania Academy under Daniel Garber and Philip Hale. In New York 1913–15, working at commercial art and studying briefly with Robert Henri. After his return to Toronto he sketched in northern Ontario 1915 and 1916 and painted air force activities in Canada for the Canadian War Memorials 1918–19. Accompanied the "box-car" painting trips to Algoma 1918 and 1919 with Harris*, MacDonald* and Jackson*. Original member of the Group of Seven 1920. Principal of the Winnipeg School of Art 1922–4 and painted in the Rocky Mountains. Returned to Toronto 1924, left the Group of Seven and taught at the Ontario College of Art 1927–9. His work after 1926 was signed "Franz Johnston." Visited the Arctic 1939, then settled at Wyebridge, Ontario. Had a summer art school on Georgian Bay from 1940. Died in Toronto.

Paul Kane 1810–1871 (14–15)

Born at Mallow, Co. Cork, the son of an English soldier serving in Ireland; the family emigrated to Canada c.1819. Attended the District Grammar School at York (Toronto) where he had lessons from a drawing-master, Drury. In his youth he worked at decorating furniture in Toronto and Cobourg and painting portraits at the latter place. Went to the United States, working as an itinerant painter south from Detroit, and sailing from New Orleans to Marseille 1841. Copied in the museums of Italy and visited Paris and London (1842–3) where he met George Catlin. On his return he painted at Mobile, Alabama, 1843–5. On arriving back at Toronto 1845 he painted the Indians and their life on a trip to Georgian Bay, Manitoulin Island and Lake Michigan. In 1846 he joined a Hudson's Bay Company annual fur-trade brigade, visiting Fort William, Fort Garry, Norway House and Fort Edmonton and reaching Fort Vancouver in the Oregon country by December. Went to Fort Victoria in April 1847 and on the return journey passed through Fort Edmonton, Fort Pitt and Norway House, returning to Toronto October 1848. On the trip he kept a journal which he published in London 1859, *The Wanderings of an Artist,* and made many sketches. Spent the rest of his life in Toronto, filling several large commissions for canvases after the sketches. Died in Toronto.

Monograph: J. Russell Harper, *Paul Kane's Frontier,* Toronto, University of Toronto Press, 1971.

Cornelius Krieghoff 1815–1872 (17–19)

Born in Amsterdam, the son of a resident of Düsseldorf then working in Holland; his mother was Dutch. In his youth he lived at Düsseldorf and near Schweinfurth in Bavaria. He is said to have gone to school in Rotterdam; but his style in painting bears the marks of the Düsseldorf Academy. As a young man he travelled in Europe as an itinerant musician and artist. Emigrated to New York 1837, enlisted in the United States Army and made (lost) records of the Seminole War. Left the army 1840 and married a woman from Longueuil (near Montreal). Spent brief periods at Rochester and Toronto but was at Longueuil by 1844 and in Montreal by 1849. Moved 1853 to Quebec, where he sold his scenes of Canadian life to officers of the garrison and others as souvenirs. Visited Europe c.1854–5 and possibly 1862 and 1869. Went to live c.1867 with a daughter in Chicago, where he died after re-visiting Montreal and Quebec 1871.

Monograph: Marius Barbeau, *Cornelius Krieghoff, Pioneer Painter of North America*, Toronto, Macmillan, 1934.

Ludger Larose 1868–1915 (*36*)

Born in Montreal. Studied painting with Abbé Joseph Chabert at the Council of Arts and Manufactures (Monument National), Montreal. Went to Paris 1887 and studied at the École des Beaux-Arts 1887–94 under Jean-Paul Laurens and Gustave Moreau; also copied old-master paintings in Rome. After his return to Montreal he taught at the École du Plateau 1894–1910 and in the Westmount schools 1912–15. Painted murals in the Sacré-Cœur chapel of Notre-Dame, Montreal. Died in Montreal.

Ozias Leduc 1864–1955 (*32*)

Born at Saint-Hilaire on the Richelieu, near Montreal. Mainly self-taught in painting, though he worked at church decoration with an Italian painter in Canada Luigi Cappello (c.1880) and with the Canadian painter Adolphe Rho (at Yamachiche, Quebec, 1883). He then began an independent career as painter of church decorations. Visited France 1897 in company with Suzor-Côté* and was there influenced by René Menard, Alfons Mucha and Henri-Eugène Le Sidaner. Returned to Saint-Hilaire where he lived a secluded life of great simplicity. His many later church paintings show the influence of Maurice Denis. Also painted still life, portraits and landscape, and made book illustrations. In later life he was the teacher of Paul-Émile Borduas, leading painter of the School of Montreal in the 1940s. Died at Saint-Hilaire.

Joseph Légaré 1795–1855 (*9–10*)

Born in Quebec. Was self-taught in painting, mainly through restoring the collection of old-master paintings brought to Canada by the two abbés Desjardins, *émigré* priests from France. He later acquired some of the canvases, exhibited them in Quebec, and sold some to the Université Laval. Was apparently involved in the Rebellion of 1837–8 and imprisoned for a brief period. Later, as a supporter of Louis-Joseph Papineau, when the latter re-entered politics 1847, he stood for election to the Legislative Assembly 1848 but was defeated. Was appointed to the Legislative Council of Canada shortly before his death in Quebec. Painted historical subjects, including romantic episodes of Indian life, landscapes and religious subjects.

Arthur Lismer 1885–1969 (*65–66*)

Born in Sheffield, Yorkshire. Studied at the Sheffield School of Art 1899–1906, working also as a newspaper illustrator. Studied at the Antwerp Academy 1906–8, returning to open his own commercial art studio in Sheffield. Emigrated to Toronto 1911 and worked for the firm of Grip Ltd. Sketched on Georgian Bay 1914 and Algonquin Park with Thomson*, Jackson* and Varley*. Taught summer art courses at the Ontario College of Art, 1913–16 and was principal of the Nova Scotia College of Art, Halifax, 1916–19. While in Halifax he painted naval activities for the Canadian War Memorials 1917–19. Returned to Toronto 1919 and taught at the Ontario College of Art 1920–7. Original member of the Group of Seven 1920. Made many sketching trips: to northern Ontario, the lower St. Lawrence, the Gaspé, Nova Scotia, Newfoundland, the Rocky Mountains, etc. Directed a children's art program at the Art Gallery of Toronto 1920–36 and as an authority on child art visited South Africa 1936–7 and taught at Columbia University, New York, 1938–9. Directed the educational work of the National Gallery of Canada 1939–40, then became principal of the school of the Art Association of Montreal 1940, teaching also at McGill University. RCA 1946. Died in Montreal.

Monograph: J. B. McLeigh, *September Gale, a Study of Arthur Lismer*, Toronto, Dent, 1955.

Frère Luc (Claude François) 1614–1685 (*1*)

Born at Amiens, the son of a cloth-worker. Began as an artist by copying religious pictures in churches and working with itinerant artists. Studied in Paris under Simon Vouet 1632 and afterwards went to Rome where, in company with Claude Lorraine, Poussin and François Perrier, he copied the works of Raphael and Guido Reni. Returned to Paris 1638 to assist Poussin in the projected decoration of the Louvre. Joined the Récollet Order 1644 and lived 1645–70 at its monastery in Paris, painting for a number of churches and making tapestry designs. In 1670 he accompanied a group from his Order to Quebec and there prepared plans for the Récollet monastery and the Séminaire de Québec. Also painted a number of religious pictures and portraits in Canada and continued to supply these to the colony after his return to France 1671. Died in Paris.

Monograph: Gérard Morisset, *La vie et l'œuvre du Frère Luc*, Quebec, Médium, 1944.

James Edward Hervey MacDonald 1873–1932 (*41–44*)

Born in Durham (England); the family (with Canadian roots) emigrated to Hamilton, Ontario, 1887. Studied at the Hamilton Art School. After the family moved to Toronto 1889 he was apprenticed to a lithographing firm and attended evening classes at the Central Ontario School of Art. Began work as a lithographer 1893 and joined the commercial art firm of Grip Ltd. 1894. Worked at book design at Carlton Studios in London 1904–7 and on his return began to sketch in and around Toronto. Made his first painting trips to northern Ontario 1909 and Georgian Bay 1910. Encouraged by Harris*, he became a full-time painter 1911 and moved to the village of Thornhill 1912. In 1913, with Harris, he visited the exhibition of Scandinavian painting in Buffalo. Sketched with Harris in the Laurentians 1913 and with Harris, Thomson* and others in Algonquin Park 1914. Went on the "box-car" sketching trips to Algoma 1918 and 1919 with Harris, Jackson* and Johnston*. Original member of the Group of Seven 1920. Taught at the Ontario College of Art, Toronto, from 1921; principal 1929–32. RCA 1931. Carried out several schemes of mural decoration in Toronto and made painting trips to Nova Scotia 1922, the Rocky Mountains 1924 ff., and the West Indies 1932. Died in Toronto.

Monograph: E. R. Hunter, *J. E. H. MacDonald*, Toronto, Ryerson Press, 1940.

David Brown Milne 1882–1953 (*56–59*)

Born near Paisley, Ontario. Taught at a country school in Bruce County before going to New York 1904. Studied for a time at the Art Students League and afterwards worked at commercial art in New York. Painted in and around New York and was apparently somewhat influenced by Maurice Prendergast and Ernest Lawson. Exhibited at the Armory Show, New York, 1913. Settled at Boston Corner in the Berkshires 1915. Enlisted in the Canadian army 1917 and painted for the Canadian War Memorials 1918. Returned to Boston Corner 1919 and until 1923 he painted there, going to the Adirondacks for the summers. Spent the winter 1923–4 in Montreal and Ottawa, returning to live in the Adirondacks. Finally returned to Canada 1928, living first at Weston, Ontario 1928–9, then at Palgrave 1929–32, Six Mile Lake on the Severn River 1932–9, Toronto 1939–40 and Uxbridge 1940–52, with summers and autumns latterly in the Haliburton district. Died in Toronto.

Monograph: Alan Jarvis, *David Milne*, Toronto, McClelland and Stewart, 1962.

James Wilson Morrice 1865–1924 (*33–34*)

Born in Montreal, the son of a Scottish textile merchant. Began sketching in watercolors 1882. Attended the University of Toronto 1882–6 and studied law in Toronto 1886–9. In Paris from 1890, studying briefly at the Académie Julian and later with Henri Harpignies; was influenced by Whistler. In his early period he painted in Italy and Belgium and on the coasts of Normandy and Brittany. Lived most of his life in Paris, paying Christmas visits (until 1914) to his parents in Montreal and sketching there and Quebec and along the St. Lawrence. On his numerous painting trips in Europe he met or worked with Maurice Prendergast and Charles Conder (1891), William Glackens and Robert Henri (1896) and Maurice Cullen* (1896–7 and 1902). From 1910 he also painted in North Africa: was at Tangier 1912–13 at the same time as Matisse, Camoin and Marquet; also painted at Marrakech and Tunis. RCA 1913. Visited Cuba 1915. Painted in France for the Canadian War Memorials 1918. Painted in the West Indies 1920–1. Died in Tunis.

Monograph: Donald W. Buchanan, *James Wilson Morrice,* Toronto, Ryerson Press, 1936.

Lucius Richard O'Brien 1832–1899 (*21–23*)

Born at Shanty Bay, the son of one of the founders of that settlement on Lake Simcoe (Ontario). Attended Upper Canada College, Toronto, and entered an architect's office c.1847. He later studied and then practised civil engineering. By 1856 in Toronto, describing himself as an artist but returned to engineering. Was a full-time artist by 1872, painting landscapes in Ontario and Quebec. Was influenced by the American painter Albert Bierstadt whom both Lord Dufferin and Lord Lorne (governors general 1872–8 and 1878–83 respectively) had invited to Canada. Was the main organizer of the Royal Canadian Academy for Lorne in 1880 and its first president (1880–90). As picture editor of G. M. Grant's *Picturesque Canada* (1882) he organized a number of artists to cover Canada from coast to coast, himself preparing a number of views for the wood-engraver. Visited the Rocky Mountains 1882 and 1886 and painted on the Pacific coast 1888. Died presumably in Toronto.

William Raphael 1833–1914 (*25*)

Born of Jewish parents in Prussia and studied at the Berlin Academy 1854–5. Emigrated to New York 1856 and painted a few portraits there. Moved to Canada 1857 and painted portraits in Quebec and Montreal. Lived chiefly in Montreal but was active at Murray Bay 1878, Saint-Hyacinthe 1886, Sherbrooke 1894–8 and Stanbridge 1905. Taught privately and in the Montreal secondary schools. Founding member of the Society of Canadian Artists, Montreal, 1867, and charter RCA 1880. Published a volume of lithographs of his drawings c.1895. Died in Montreal.

Marc-Aurèle de Foy Suzor-Côtè 1869–1937 (*37*)

Born at Arthabaska, Quebec (the son of Théophile Côté and Cécile de Foy-Suzor). Began as a painter by assisting the painter Maxime Rousseau in the decoration of the church at Arthabaska. Went to Paris 1890 and studied at the Julian and Colarossi academies and at the École des Beaux-Arts. Was influenced by the Impressionists before his return to Montreal 1893. Was again in France from the later 1890s, returning to open a studio in Montreal 1908. Spent most summers painting at Arthabaska. Died at Daytona Beach, Florida, where he had gone for his health.

Tom (Thomas John) Thomson 1877–1917 (*45–51*)

Born on a farm near Claremont, Ontario; the family later moved to Leith, near Owen Sound on Georgian Bay. Became a machinist's apprentice 1899, then attended business school at Chatham, Ontario, 1900. Lived 1901–5 in Seattle, where his brother kept a business school; worked at photo-engraving and began to sketch. On his return to Canada c.1904 he worked at photo-engraving and commercial art, in 1907 joining the firm of Grip Ltd., where he met MacDonald*. Probably had a few painting lessons from William Cruikshank; began to sketch in oils. Made short sketching trips near Toronto 1911 and his first trip to Algonquin Park 1912; also visited Mississauga Forest Reserve 1912. Worked for the commercial art firm of Rous & Mann 1912–1914, exhibited his first canvas 1913 and in 1914 was encouraged to paint full time by Harris* and Dr. J. M. MacCallum, a patron of artists. Painted at Canoe Lake, Algonquin Park, 1914, with Jackson*, MacDonald, Lismer* and Varley*. Spent most of his time 1914–17 in Algonquin Park, working intermittently as a fire-ranger and returning in the winters to paint in a shack beside the Studio Building, Toronto. Was drowned in Canoe Lake in July 1917.

Monograph: Joan Murray, *The Art of Tom Thomson* (exhibition catalogue) Toronto, Art Gallery of Ontario, 1971.

Robert Clow Todd 1809–c.1865 (13)

Born in England, possibly at Berwick-upon-Tweed. Worked as carriage-painter in London and Edinburgh. Emigrated to Canada 1834 and set up in Quebec as a "house, carriage and ornamental painter." By 1841 he was doing carving and gilding. Lived briefly on a farm at Montmorency near Quebec but moved c.1854 to Toronto where he advertised himself as "artist, herald and ornamental painter," and later simply as artist. Several of his comparatively rare paintings have backgrounds of Montmorency Falls and were probably commissioned as horse portraits. Died in Toronto.

Frederick Horsman Varley 1881–1969 (53–55)

Born in Sheffield, Yorkshire. Began his studies in design at the Sheffield School of Art at the age of twelve but by the time of his graduation 1899 had turned to painting. Studied at the Antwerp Academy 1900–2, then worked in London as an illustrator, returning to Sheffield 1908. Emigrated to Canada 1912, working in Toronto as a commercial artist at Grip Ltd. (1912) and later at Rous & Mann until 1917. Made his first sketching trip to Algonquin Park 1914 with Thomson*, Lismer*, Jackson* and others. Painted in France for the Canadian War Memorials 1918–19, returning to Toronto where he painted a number of portraits, as he did throughout his career. Original member of the Group of Seven 1920. Taught at the Ontario College of Art, Toronto, 1925–6. In Vancouver 1926–36, teaching first at the Vancouver School of Art and then at his own school from 1933. Lived in Ottawa 1936–40 and taught at the Ottawa Art Association. Visited the Arctic 1938. In Montreal 1940–4, then Ottawa, and settled in Toronto 1945. Died in Toronto.

Frederick Arthur Verner 1836–1928 (26)

Born at Sheridan (near Oakville, Ontario), the son of the principal of the grammar school there. Went to London 1856 and studied at Leigh's School of Art and South Kensington Art School. Served in the British Army for several years and fought in Italy with Garibaldi's volunteer army 1860–1. Returned to Canada 1862, opened a studio in Toronto and began his extensive travels to the west, which took him to the prairies and eventually to the Rocky Mountains. Besides landscapes, he painted many pictures of buffalo and made portraits of the treaty conferences with the Indians in Manitoba. Also worked at coloring photographs for the Notman studios in Toronto. Was at Windsor, Ontario, 1870. Founding member of the Ontario Society of Artists 1872. Went to England 1880, returning in the late 1880s to Windsor, Ontario. Spent his latter years with a nephew in London, where he died; the house in Fulham Palace Road was destroyed, along with a number of his works, in the Second World War.

Homer Ranford Watson 1855–1936 (*30–31*)

Born at the village of Doon (near Kitchener, Ontario), the son of a miller. Early turned to art and worked in Toronto 1874–5 for the Notman photographic studio. Began his study of painting by copying portraits in Toronto. In New York 1876–7 he saw paintings by the Hudson River School, painted in the Adirondacks and presumably met George Inness. After his return to Doon he worked as an illustrator, exhibited in Toronto and was encouraged to paint by the purchase 1880 of a canvas by Lord Lorne (Governor General of Canada) for Queen Victoria. RCA 1882. In Toronto 1882 met Oscar Wilde, who called him the "Canadian Constable" and later introduced him to Whistler in London. On a visit to England and Scotland 1887–9 he saw paintings by the Barbizon School and became friends with Sir George Clausen, E. J. Gregory and other artists. After another visit to London 1891 he essayed a grander and more monumental style inspired by Constable. Sketched with Horatio Walker on the Ile d'Orléans 1896. Visited London several times between 1897 and 1910 and Cape Breton Island 1909. Painted for the Canadian War Memorials 1918. PRCA 1918–22. Visited the Rocky Mountains 1929. Died at Doon.

Monograph: J. Russell Harper, *Homer Watson* (exhibition catalogue), Ottawa, National Gallery of Canada, 1963.

Robert Reginald Whale 1805–1887 (*12*)

Born at Altarnun, Cornwall. At an early age he studied portraits by Reynolds in the National Gallery, London, returning to set himself up as a portrait painter in Cornwall. Emigrated to Canada, settling first at Burford (Ontario) 1852 and Brantford in 1864. Revisited England several times. Carried out commissions for portraits and landscapes in southern Ontario; also painted a variety of other subjects, which he exhibited at provincial exhibitions, and for which he won prizes. Made a moving "panorama" of the Indian Mutiny which he exhibited widely in his district. Died at Brantford.